HOME WINEMAKING CHEM 101

-IRIO

HOME WINEMAKING CHEM 101

Curtis W. Irion, Ph.D

To order additional copies of this book, contact:

Xlibris Corporation

1-888-7-XLIBRIS

www.Xlibris.com

Orders@Xlibris.com

CONTENTS

INTRODUCTION

Home winemaking has been an art that has been practiced and handed down by many families for literally generations. All sorts of recipes exist and one can certainly be proud when all of their time and patience produces a wine which can be appreciated and enjoyed by others. Now home winemaking is increasing in popularity at an amazing rate as adults are seeing that with proper techniques it really is not that difficult to do and it is actually a lot of fun. What is also quite nice is that it is perfectly legal! The Federal Bureau of Firearms, Tobacco, and Alcohol allows any adult living in a household to legally produce 100 gallons of wine per year. If two or more adults live in the household, then up to 200 gallons may be produced. The only real stipulation is that none of it may be sold which of course makes perfect sense. But a note of caution is that the Bureau defines an adult as anyone who is legally old enough to consume alcohol, so in the United States this means you must actually be 21 or older to make your own wine.

Many books have been written explaining the basic procedures of making wine at home and most of them do offer valuable step by step ways to make wine. Unfortunately, what they do not seem to accomplish is to explain the basic biology and chemistry of what is happening in the detailed process of grapes turning into wine. Sure books are available explaining the chemical and biochemical processes, but they are generally advanced texts suitable for enology (winemaking) students or the professional winemaker. Few home winemakers fall into these categories, yet I believe that a majority of those making wines at home would at least like to have a basic idea of what's going on as the grapes slowly, yet miraculously change into wine.

My interest in home winemaking is quite easy to understand. I truly enjoy the experience of making wine at home from not only grapes but also other fruits. I am also a biologist and a chemist and as such find all aspects of winemaking quite fascinating. I am also quite aware that not all home winemakers are scientists or even have any desire to be involved in scientific fields. So, what I have attempted to accomplish is to produce a book which is easy to understand by just about anyone who is interested in what is occurring chemically as grapes change into wine. I have also attempted to show the basic chemical reactions which occur as one goes through all of the stages of home winemaking. By understanding the basic chemical principles involved, as well as simple measurements, one should be able to consistently produce clear, well tasting wines. Finally, no matter how careful we are, problems are often encountered which may negatively influence the outcome of our hard work. When we deal with biological organisms such as yeast, and mess around with chemicals, we certainly should expect an occasional problem to arise. But, all may not be lost since all kinds of remedies exist which can take an awful tasting wine and make it quite drinkable. So, when taking this into consideration, I have devoted the last chapter of the book to trying to identify the more common problems encountered in home winemaking and have attempted to show how each potential problem can be rectified through sound chemical principles. With this in mind, I hope the reader finds that a little chemistry can go a long way in helping to make home winemaking just a little bit more productive and interesting.

DEDICATION

The writing of most books involving both biology and chemistry requires the author to be able to actively research the current trends in what one is seeking to investigate. I have been most fortunate in that I have at my disposal two excellent universities which offer a wide assortment of information dealing with the biology and chemistry of winemaking. Without a doubt, the University of Pittsburgh is a major research university with which I have spent countless hours investigating winemaking and as a sidelight, medical research. I have also spent much time at the more agricultural based Pennsylvania State University studying in depth the specific relationships between grapes and wine. I am quite appreciative of all of the help offered to me at these two fine universities.

I would also like to express my appreciation to the numerous wineries located along the shores of Lake Erie which produce excellent LABRUSCA, French-hybrid, and even VINIFERA wines. They all offer many of their juices for sale to the home winemaker as well as sound advise.

It is always good to know someone who really has a unique ability to be gifted in making a certain craft. Such is the case for Ed Scott who has the natural ability to consistently produce ribbon winning wines and has given me much insight into the home winemaking process. I certainly appreciate his help. Finally, I would like to thank my family for all of their support and honesty as I try to continually hone my winemaking skills.

CHAPTER 1

The Basic Chemistry of Grapes and Fermentation

> "Wine has been with us since the beginning of civilization. It is the temperate, civilized, sacred, romantic mealtime beverage recommended in the Bible. Wine has been praised for centuries by statesmen, philosophers, poets, and scholars. Wine in moderation is an integral part of our culture, heritage, and gracious way of life" Robert Mondavi

An incredible diversity of plants and animals occupy our planet, yet they only make up part of the living creatures of the world. Microscopic organisms such as bacteria and yeast are found in every breath that we take since they exist floating naturally about in the air we breathe. Living organisms tend to interact with one another forming all kinds of harmonious relationships. A truly classic example can be observed through the harmony between humans, grapes, yeast, and bacteria. For well over five thousand years these characters have been helping in making one of natures most natural beverages, wine!

The Chemistry of the Universe

It really does not matter if we are talking about plants, animals, or even rocks since everything in existence is governed by certain chemical laws and physical properties. A simplified understanding of some of these concepts is just what the home winemaker needs to put this hobby into an excitingly new perspective.

Elements and Atoms

All substances and organisms found on earth are made up of combinations of the elements which make up the universe. In dealing with simplified chemistry, it is just fine and dandy to call elements by their more common name, atoms. Each atom is unique in that it contains a certain number of submicroscopic particles called protons, neutrons, and electrons. These extremely small particles carry different attractive charges which help to hold the atom together. Being a tad more specific, the nucleus of an atom contains positively charged protons and neutrally charged neutrons. Spinning around the nucleus are the negatively charged electrons which are drawn toward the nucleus by the larger positively charged protons. It is sort of like a magnetic attraction and it keeps the atom together

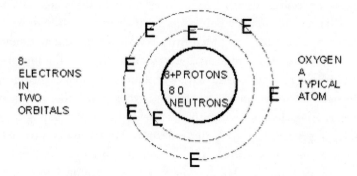

What makes each atom different is the amounts of protons, neutrons, and electrons that it contains. For example hydrogen is the smallest atom with only one proton and one neutron. It is so simple that it does not even contain a neutron. On the other hand the largest natural atom is uranium with 92 protons, 146 neutrons, and 92 electrons. Now that to be sure is a big difference in size!

Chemical Reactions

Sure, atoms are neat if one is a chemist but what do they have to do with turning grapes into wine? The answer lies in the simple fact that both grapes and wine are made up of combinations of these atoms forming some very interesting substances which we shall soon examine. These substances, and actually all of the substances of the universe are able to exist because most atoms are downright unstable. To simply put it, atoms are either in need of more electrons or need to get rid of some electrons for chemical stability to occur. As shown in the above illustration, the electrons revolve around the nucleus in well defined electron orbitals with each orbital only holding a specific number of electrons. Our concern is really only the outermost orbital since here is where electrons are either given off or accepted by other atoms. From the world of chemistry, we know that for an atom to be chemically stable, it must have eight electrons in that outermost orbital. This is true for all atoms except for hydrogen and helium which are so small that they only need two electrons for maximum stability.

As is often true, oddballs always seem to exist in the universe! So without getting too carried away, atoms are always giving up electrons to other atoms, accepting electrons from other atoms, or even sharing electrons with other atoms in their never ending quest of having eight electrons in this outermost orbital. When this grabbing, giving, or sharing occurs, the atoms become attracted to each other forming what we know by the common names molecules, molecular substances, or even compounds. Here is a quite common and simplified example of the grabbing and accepting and the sodium chloride (table salt) molecule which is formed by this reaction.

THE MAKING OF SALT

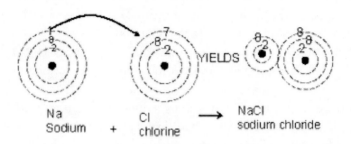

Na   Cl   NaCl
Sodium   +   chlorine   →   sodium chloride

Building Blocks of Wine

Although table salt is an inorganic compound, grapes are made up mostly of organic compounds which contain both carbon and hydrogen. They are known as hydrocarbons and make up most of the structural material of plants, animals, and that little fungus known as yeast. These hydrocarbons also attract other atoms forming all sorts of nifty molecules which make grapes and wines quite unique. In fact, with modern analytical techniques, chemists are now aware that over 10,000 different substances exist in the wines of the world! Fortunately for the home winemaker, only a small number of them need to be understood in order to appreciate the basic chemistry of wine. Most of the other thousands of chemicals are unique to each grape variety and are only found in very small amounts and so do not need to be examined unless you are truly a chemistry fanatic!

C,H,N,O,P,S

No matter what type of living organism one studies, six common atoms make up the majority of the substances found in their cells. We call them C,H,N,O,P,S which refers to their chemical symbols on the periodical chart of the elements.

Carbon (C) is the major atom of organic life and carbon tends to bond to other carbon atoms forming carbon linked chains which attract other atoms to them. These carbon based molecules form the many tastes and odors of wine.

Hydrogen (H) of course is a primary atom in water (H_2O) but it is also readily attracted to carbon atoms forming many different hydrocarbons.

Nitrogen (N) is the most common atom in the atmosphere but it is also attracted to carbon, hydrogen, and oxygen forming the amino acids of nature which link together to form proteins. Proteins are the main structural compounds found in all living organisms and grapes contain them in varying amounts.

Oxygen (O) is of course also found in water but it is also attracted to carbon forming the various hydrocarbons found in grapes and wine.

Phosphorous (P) is commonly found in all living cells and it makes up the cell's main energy storing molecule known simply as ATP. The P stands for phosphate (which contains phosphorous) and ATP molecules are always being formed and then broken down freeing up their large supply of energy for cellular functions.

Sulfur (S) is the well known stinky smelling atom but it is found in three of the twenty existing amino acids and so is an integral part of many different kinds of proteins including grape proteins.

C, H, N, O, P, S in Grapes and Wine

C—glucose, fructose, fatty acids, proteins, ethyl alcohol, acetaldehyde, glycerol, acids, esters, tannins, pigments, resveratrol, fusel oils

H—glucose, fructose, fatty acids, proteins, ethyl alcohol, acetaldehyde, glycerol, acids, esters, tannins, pigments, resveratrol, fusel oils

N—proteins, histamines, esters

O—glucose, fructose, ethyl alcohol, acetaldehyde, proteins, esters, organic acids, glycerol, tannins, pigments, resveratrol, fusel oils

P—ATP for energy making

S—proteins, nasty sulfur compounds

Benzene—An Unusual Cyclic Hydrocarbon

Benzene is indeed a strange organic hydrocarbon with the simple formula C_6H_6. What makes it kind of strange is that the carbon atoms are attracted to each other in a cyclic manner. Hence it is called a cyclic hydrocarbon!

Many people are quite aware that benzene by itself is actually a poisonous compound found in car exhaust and cigarette smoke. That is very much true but benzene also has a good side to it. Plants, including grapes, actually can synthesize benzene and re-arrange it into many different kinds of good phenolic compounds.

THE MAKING OF BENZENE INTO A GOOD SUBSTANCE

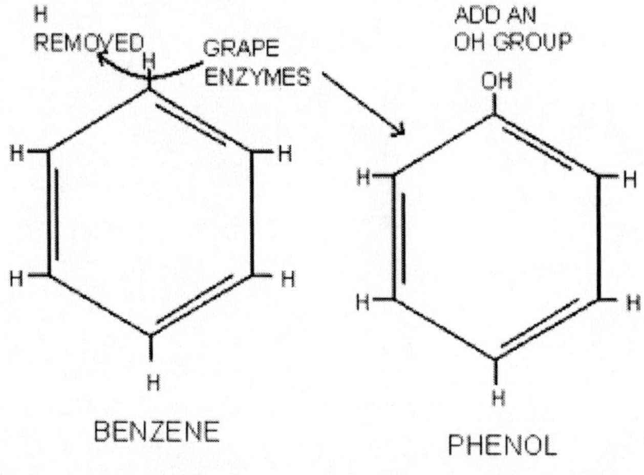

BENZENE

PHENOL

Actually the phenols produced by certain plants are receiving lots of positive publicity since they neutralize poisons (free radicals) in the human body. These good phenols are found in significant amounts in two very commonly consumed beverages, green tea and WINE!

Water and Wine

Living cells are loaded with water molecules and water chemically acts as one big magnet in that it attracts all sorts of substances towards it. This occurs due to the fact that water is natuarally a polar substance in that it has both positive and negative areas on the molecule. In a water molecule, the two hydrogen atoms are attracted to the oxygen atom through the sharing of electrons but this sharing of electrons is not exactly equal. Without getting into detailed chemistry, the area around the oxygen atom actually has a greater pulling power for the shared electrons and this then gives the oxygen atom a slight negative charge. In order to even things out, the immediate area around the hydrogen atoms then have a slight positive charge. So water truly is a polar substance and this is also true for most of the other substances found in grapes and wine. As a result, most of the substances found in grapes and the resulting wine are attracted to water and so readily dissolve in it.

ETHYL ALCOHOL IS ATTRACTED TO WATER LIKE A MAGNET

The Role of pH

Many factors are certainly involved in taking grapes and making a truly decent tasting wine. The quality of the grapes, sterilization, fermenting techniques, and even a bit of good luck play some role in the final transformation of grapes to wine. However, to many enologists (winemakers), one of the most important factors in producing a quality wine is understanding the concept of pH and using the knowledge of it wisely throughout the entire process. The term pH refers to the "power of hydrogen" and is actually an indicator of how much acid or base is present in a given solution. When atoms give up or accept electrons, they become what are known as ions. If you lose an electron you pick up a positive charge and if you grab an electron you pick up a negative charge. This of course is what is occurring when sodium gives an electron to chlorine forming sodium chloride (table salt) and it also relates well to understanding pH. So, in getting back to pH, an easy to understand definition of an acid is any substance that releases hydrogen ions (H+) when placed in water. A base releases hydroxyl ions (OH-) when placed in water. The amount of H+ in a solution shows how acidic it is and the amount of OH—shows the actual strength of the base. So, to put it into total perspective, we can measure the strength of acids and bases by using a pH scale which is based on a numbering system from 0 to 14 with a pH of 7 considered to be a neutral solution containing equal amounts of acids and bases.

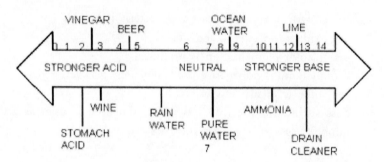

THE pH SCALE

Grapes, and other fruits, contain many more acids than bases so their natural pH is on the acidic side. Yet, they are weak acids in that only a small proportion of these acids actually release their hydrogen ions. Most of them instead just exist in the grape, and the resultant wine, as the entire acid still containing all of their hydrogens. But enough do release some of their hydrogen ions thus maintaining an acid condition and enologists strive to keep a pH between 3.0 and 3.5 in their musts and wines. This can be done by ensuring that the proper amount of two weak acids, commonly found in grapes, are contained in the fermenting must. These two weak acids are known as tartaric and malic acid and as we will definitely see, both heavily influence the success of entire winemaking process.

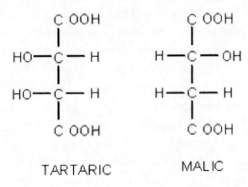

THE TWO COMMON ACIDS IN GRAPES AND WINES

TARTARIC   MALIC

The Benefits of Maintaining a Must pH Between 3.0 and 3.5

1. the growth of spoilage yeast and bacteria is halted.
2. less oxidation occurs to the wine.
3. better color pigmentation is produced.
4. various tannins polymerize (stick together) at a faster rate.
5. less stuck fermentations occur
6. Less sulfur dioxide (SO_2) is required which is used as an inhibitor of spoilage yeast and bacteria.

7. less rotten-egg smelling hydrogen sulfide (H_2S) is produced along with its other nasty smelling sulfur chemical relatives.
8. less fining ingredients are necessary before bottling the wine.
9. One becomes a happier, more satisfied amateur enologist!

Maintaining the correct wine pH can easily be accomplished but one really needs to purchase a neat, inexpensive chemistry gadget to be truly accurate in consistently determining pH. It is a portable, digital pH meter which only has to be turned on, placed in the juice or wine and it will readily determine how many H+ ions they contain by giving the exact pH reading. They are well worth the investment since keeping that constant pH between 3.0 and 3.5 is highly important in producing a sound wine year after year.

The Fermentation Chemistry of Wine

All living organisms need to make energy and most of them are aerobic in that oxygen is needed in the overall process. These aerobes take in sugar, and with the use of oxygen, convert it into energy and two waste products. The basic chemical reaction is as noted below.

$$C_6H_{12}O_6 + 6O_2 \rightarrow 6CO_2 + 6H_2O + energy$$

glucose + oxygen→carbon dioxide + water + energy

In this aerobic respiration reaction, 304 kilocalories of energy is generated from the breakdown of an individual glucose molecule. This translates into a net gain of 36 ATP molecules which is how aerobic organisms are able to store energy for later use. However, luckily for the winemaker, not all living organisms need oxygen in order to produce energy. For example, yeast are small microscopic fungi and some of them, especially wine yeast, carry on a process called fermentation in order to meet their minimal energy requirements. Actually the process of fermentation is a very simple chemical reaction.

$$C_6H_{12}O_6 \rightarrow 2C_2H_5OH + 2CO_2 + energy$$

glucose $\rightarrow$ ethyl alcohol + carbon dioxide + energy

Yeast, being single celled, really don't require much energy and this fermentation reaction only produces 16 kilocalories of energy and two ATP molecules. But, that is certainly enough for each yeast cell and it allows them to grow and divide very quickly. The ethyl alcohol produced is actually a waste product that the yeast must excrete, so when we drink wine, we are actually drinking yeast waste! Fancy that or a moment! Of course, all winemakers realize that yeast are necessary in producing wine and many actually just use the native wild yeasts which are naturally present on the grapes at harvest to ferment their grapes. These yeast strains are typically KLOECKERA APICULATA and CANDIDA STELLATAONG with roughly seven or so other species. Although they will naturally ferment grapes, most winemakers prefer to use the so-called wine yeast, SACCHAROMYCES CERVISIAE which is much easier to use and control. This yeast strain is believed to have been isolated from an oak tree many years ago and modern genetics have produced many varieties of this most unusual yeast which has led to the production of many great wines.

The major producers are Lalvin, Red Star, and Vintner's Choice. All three offer many of the same varieties but with somewhat different names.

Commonly Used Wine Yeast

Wine Yeast	Type of Wine	Characteristics
Montrachet	reds, whites	strong fermenter, tolerates SO_2, does not work well if sugar is higher than 23.5%, may cause stuck fermentations, implicated in H2S production
Pasteur Champagne	reds, whites	ferments quickly, tolerates low temperatures, SO_2, and high alcohol, ferments to dryness, restarts stuck fermentations
Cotes Des Blanc	fruity whites, blush, fruit wines	produces pleasant esters, slow fermenter, low foaming, ferments well at 50 - 70 °F, sensitive to high alcohol
Prise de Mousse	reds, whites	ferments vigorously, ferments to dryness, tolerates SO_2 and high alcohol, low foaming, ferments well at low temperatures, produces compact lees
Steinberg	German grapes	ferments well at low temperatures, produces complex fruit odors, sensitive to SO_2, slow fermentation, produces floral wines

Wine Yeast	Type of Wine	Characteristics
Pasteur Red	full bodied reds	tolerates high temperatures and SO2, extracts pigments well, vigorous fermenter, seldom produces a stuck fermentation
Lalvin ICV D-47	whites, rose	low foaming, fast fermenter, ferments well at 50 - 86°F, produces compact lees
Lalvin EC-118	all types	low foaming, low production of volatile acids, low H2S production, ferments well at 45 - 90°F, tolerates high initial sugar levels and high alcohol, good for restarting stuck fermentations
Lalvin 71B 1122	young wines, rose, residual sugar whites	rapid fermentation, ferments well at 59 - 86°F, may metabolize 20 - 40% of the malic acid in the must so is great for high acid wines, produces pleasant esters
Lalvin K1V-1116	all wines including fruits	rapid and complete fermenter, ferments well at 59 - 86°F, grows well in low nutrient musts, tolerates SO2 and high sugar levels, restarts stuck fermentations

Stuck Fermentation

Many initial home winemakers think that all one has to do is buy some juice, add sugar and yeast, and away we go with the fermentation. But, unfortunately fermentation chemistry can be quite complex and suddenly our fermenting mixture may just quit way too early. We call this a stuck fermentation and it has probably plagued winemakers for thousands of years and still can be a nasty problem. What happens is that the wine must is fermenting quite well for many days and then it suddenly quits before all of the sugar has been metabolized by the yeast. Nobody wants this situation to occur since lots of sugar may be left, the alcohol content will be too low for storage stability, and spoilage organisms love to grow in this situation. It used to happen in the old days due mainly to extremely high fermentation temperatures which cause ethyl alcohol to accumulate inside of the cells of the yeast ultimately killing them. Currently many stuck fermentations occur due to the modern tendency of actually fermenting musts at low temperatures in order to achieve a fresh, fruity wine which is now in vogue. It also may occur due to excessive clarification of the must to achieve a brilliantly clear wine, but which may also remove many of the essential nutrients needed for extended yeast growth. It is well known that a low nitrogen nutrient supply, and too high of an initial sugar level will also cause a stuck fermentation. Finally, we are also aware that during normal yeast fermentations, two toxic mid-chained carboxylic acids are produced by yeast themselves, and if they accumulate too much, they can actually be toxic to the living yeast which are busy fermenting the must. They are known as octanoic and decanoic acids and luckily we shall see how they can be removed from the must so their potential damage can easily be negated with a very simple technique.

Fortunately, all is not lost if we experience the dreaded stuck fermentation. In fact, here is a good way to restart a stuck fermentation. First rack the must to remove possible spoilage organisms, add nitrogen supplements such as diammonium phosphate or a commercial yeast supplement, and add a yeast strain which is known to help restart stuck fermentations. Also a great idea is to also add to the must the outer shells of dead yeast known as yeast hulls or ghosts. These hulls will absorb and remove the accumultion of toxic octanoic and decanoic acids and at the same time will also provide nutrients in the form of unsaturated fatty acids and sterols which yeast cannot manufacture once anaerobic fermentation starts later on in the process.

The addition of yeast nutrients to must is commonplace but a word of caution exists when supplementing with the still often available urea compound which is basically just concentrated nitrogen and is still sold in various nutrient packages. Yeast can readily make their own urea from the amino acid arginine which is commonly found in grapes. They slowly yet naturally release small amounts of it out of their cells and into the fermenting must. Here the urea will react with ethyl alcohol forming small amounts of a substance called ethyl carbamate. In lab studies, high doses of ethyl carbamate cause cancer and so the wine industry is trying to eliminate it entirely from their products even if it is only found in very small amounts. But most home winemakers are not aware of this potential problem at all so by adding urea as an additive, they may cause way too much ethyl carbamate to be made in their otherwise natural wine. So, the obvious solution is to avoid any nutrient packets containing urea and fortunately many different nutrient packets are available without containing this substance.

THE PROBLEM WITH UREA

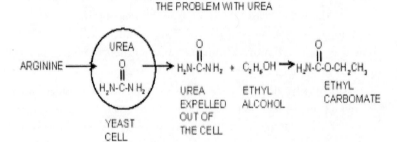

To be sure, adding a nitrogen supplement is highly recommended but it is best to stay with diammonium phosphate or some other commercial yeast nutrient packet that does not contain urea. It probably takes a high concentration of ethyl carbamate, taken into the body for many years to possibly cause cancer but its better to be safe than sorry.

Malolactic Fermentation (ML Fermentation)

It has already been previously stated, that grapes contain fair amounts of both tartaric and malic acid. This is especially true of grapes grown in cold climates where malic acid is not needed as an energy source and so tends to accumulate in the grape. On the other hand, grapes grown in warm climates such as California contain much less malic acid since much of it is used by mature grapes as an energy source due to the warm conditions which obviously increases overall grape metabolism. Unfortunately, malic acid is considered by many to be harsh tasting on the palate and so wine high in malic acid may be somewhat strong tasting. What's nice is that the home winemaker may eliminate much if not all of the malic acid from their wines by inducing a malolactic fermentation using one of the few types of bacteria that can grow at a wine pH. These are the hardy lactic acid bacteria and LEUCONOSTOC, LACTO-BACILLUS, and PEDIOCOCCUS are the scientific names for the three major types which can actively grow in grape must. It should be noted though that the last two are usually considered to be spoilage bacteria and certainly should be avoided. The good one, LEUCONOSTOC OENOS, has now been commercially cultured and can be added to musts in order to induce a malolactic fermentation. What this bacteria soon accomplishes in the must is that it is able to convert malic acid into lactic acid which is much milder on the palate and so improves the balance in the wine.

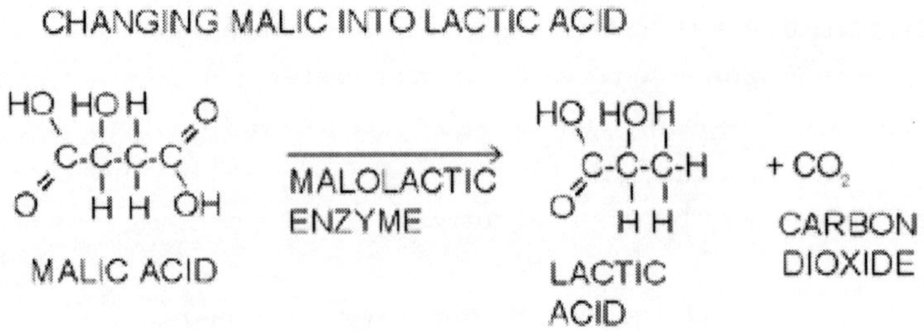

CHANGING MALIC INTO LACTIC ACID

HO HOH O
\ | | //
C-C-C-C
// | | | \
O H H OH

MALIC ACID

→ MALOLACTIC ENZYME

HO HOH
\ | | |
C-C-C-H
// | | |
O H H

LACTIC ACID

$+ CO_2$

CARBON DIOXIDE

Decisions To Be Made Involving Leuconostoc oenos

Wines which should undergo ML fermentation
- hearty reds
- red from cold climates
- whites from cold climates
- Chardonnay
- Sauvignon Blanc

Wines which do not benefit
- fruit wines
- reds from warm climates
- whites from warm climates
- wines for early consumption

LEUCONOSTOC OENOS is a tough bacteria and will readily survive and grow at a pH between 3.0 and 3.5. It is very sensitive to SO_2 but proper timing of adding the bacteria to the must may allow it to grow in low sulfited musts. At a pH above 3.5 the other spoilage lactic acid bacteria, which are not as hardy, may grow and this is not very good since they tend to metabolize sugars into acetic acid which is that good old chemical known for its vinegary taste. To make matters even worse, they can also produce some other nasty products which will be later addressed.

Malolactic Fermentation Problems Encountered at a pH greater than 3.5

- spoilage LACTOBACILLUS and PEDIOCOCCUS dominate over LEUCONOSTOC
- sugar is fermented into acetic acid (lactic souring)
- more fruity characteristics are lost
- pigment color loss is encountered
- more ethyl acetate is produced (nail polish remover or acetone smell)
- glycerol is converted into bitter tasting acrolein
- tartaric acid may be oxidized giving a sauerkraut taste
- more buttery, cheesy, milky odors are produced
- greater chance of a stuck fermentation occurring
- need more be said?

A major argument among enologists is when to actually initiate the malolactic fermentation since it can be performed anytime throughout the fermentation process. Probably for the home winemaker the best time is after the second racking since at this time period the SO_2 and sugar levels are low and the moderate alcohol concentration is not toxic to the lactic acid bacteria. Periodical racking during ML Fermentation is very important since besides removing unwanted particulate matter, it also removes from the must mid-chained carboxylic acids such as octanoic and decanoic which are produced from the breakdown of dead yeast cells. In high concentrations these acids interfere with the cellular membrane functions in both the surviving fermenting yeast and also lactic acid bacteria. It is also wise to remember that the addition of yeast hulls after racking will absorb and remove from the musts any remaining octanoic and decanoic acids so they are indeed a very positive addition. However, one negative aspect of periodical racking which is certainly good to know is that racking also removes many of the nutrients which lactic acid bacteria need to grow. So it is very important after racking to add back to the must the complex set of nutrients which these bacteria require. If possible purchase lactic acid bacteria growth nutrients or at least regular yeast nutrients which will add back to the must many essential nutrients so these bacteria can totally convert malic into lactic acids.

Although some grape musts may contain some wild strains of lactic acid bacteria it is most certainly wise to purchase specific cultures of LEUCONOSTOC OENOS. At temperatures greater than 70°F these bacteria will soon start to decarboxylate (remove a COOH group) malic acid into the much milder tasting lactic acid. What's also nice is that one can purchase a simple chromatography kit which tells the home enologist when all of the malic acid has been finally made into lactic acid. They are available at winemaking outlets. Then the only thing left to do is to destroy any remaining bacteria after everything has been said and done. It is easy to do so by sulfiting the must with 50 milligrams per liter SO_2 to ensure that the lactic acid bacteria are destroyed. They must be eliminated since they can produce cloudiness and off-flavors in the wine as the wine ages in the bottle if any are left viable (living).

CHAPTER 2. THE TRANSFORMATION OF GRAPES INTO WINE

"Wine is a living liquid containing no preservatives. Its life cycle comprises youth, maturity, old age, and death. When not treated with reasonable respect it will sicken and die."
Julia Child

Grapes belong to the VITACEAE family and 100 species exist in the scientific literature. Most likely 65 of these are genuine species and the rest are interspecific hybrids. What's kind of interesting is that of all of these species, only two make up the vast majority of the grapes which are made into wine. Even so, well over 15,000 different cultivars of grapes are known to exist, so choosing the types of grapes to be made into wine can sometimes be a chore. Depending upon where one lives only certain varieties may be available, but we now live in a small world, and the juices of many unusual varieties can be delivered to you without too much difficulty from different foreign countries. A great place to look for different varieties is the world wide web and detailed descriptions are offered for the more common types and even their availability. Also, the excellent book "How To Be A Wine Expert" by James Gabler, is a very fine reference work on classical wine varieties. Of course, one of the fascinations of the wine hobbyist is experimenting with different grape varieties and being either overjoyed or not so pleased with the ultimate outcome of each variety. Individual preferences obviously come into play but typically Europeans make their wine from VITIS VINIFERA, the so-called European grape. Americans on the other hand make wines from not only VITIS VINIFERA but also from VITIS LABRUSCA, the American grape, and also from French-American hybrids. Other species such as the southern U.S. grape, VITIS ROTUNIDIFOLIA are sometimes fermented but the above varieties are much more common. Of course, many home winemakers grow their own grapes but the vast majority probably either buy fresh juice, frozen juice, or even concentrates. They are highly available after harvest but still can be quite confusing as to what to actually purchase. Sometimes it is hard to figure out what is what but it should definitely be realized that often what we think we are buying is not necessarily the real thing! Often many juices or concentrates are really just blends of many inferior grapes that have been given a common name such as Chablis, Burgundy, and Rose. They may sound good but it is much better to buy what are called "varietal juices" which must contain at least 75% of whatever grape is contained on the label. For example, if one buys a varietal such as the popular Cabernet Sauvignon it must contain at least 75% Cabernet Sauvignon grapes which is its actual varietal name. So one must be careful in their selection since typically many of the available juice concentrates are rather generic in nature. They essentially are like the common generic jug wines, which contain small amounts of a specific grape and the rest is just inferior grapes which are not good enough for varietal status or even the commercial wine industry.

Common Varietal Grapes Typically Available For Purchase and Which Make Excellent Wines

Vitis vinifera	*Vitis labrusca*	French Hybrids
Reds	Reds	Reds
Cabernet Sauvignon	Concord	Chambourcin
Syrah	Fredonia	de Chaunac
Merlot	Catawba (pink)	Marechal Foch
Pinot Noir		Leon Millot
Zinfandel		
Whites	Whites	Whites
Chardonnay	Niagara	Delaware
Sauvignon blanc	Dutchess	Seyval blanc
Riesling	Delaware	Vidal blanc
Gewurztraminer		Vignoles

Even though one purchases sound varietal grapes, every year offers to us changes in sugars, acids, and overall flavors due to overall climatic conditions. Even each vineyard is unique in its own particular combinations of sun exposure, soil types, and nutrient availability. The French refer to this uniqueness as "Terroir" and they probably have studied this concept as much as anyone. In fact, they actually have done test trials in some of the old vineyards in France. Here they grow the same common variety year after year, and professional enologists have noted different tastes and odors from the same variety depending upon which vineyard the grapes where grown in. The French believe the number one factor for these different tastes and odors is the variations in soil found in each vineyard. So, as a result of the concept of "Terroir" and the weather patterns, it is very difficult to actually give factual definitions of the aromas and tastes one can expect to achieve from each grape variety.

The Common Substances Found in Grapes

Whatever the variety, when it really comes down to it grapes are grapes. Yes, they most certainly have their own individual molecular substances giving them certain peculiar tastes and scents, but as a whole they all possess many common chemical substances. Sure, they are mostly water but they also commonly contain sugars, acids, pectins, flavonoids, nonflavonoids, esters, minerals, vitamins, aromatics, and even some proteins. To many it is truly fascinating chemistry which occurs as the grapes are changed into wine during the entire fermentation and aging processes. Actually when one drinks a glass of wine, they are actually drinking a mixture of chemicals which by themselves may not be even discernible to our taste buds. However, in the words of a wine taster, they collectively add up to become aromatic (smell), organoleptic (influence taste perception), and sapid (influence taste and mouth feel). Although most of the pleasing aromatics are produced during fermentation, some are actually produced during the resting aging time and therefore make there own unique contribution to wines.

By far the most common aromatics are the fusel oils, volatile acids, and fatty acid esters. Such substances as phenols, terpenoids, hydrocarbons, sulfur, and nitrogen compounds are also present in rather small quantities but definitely influence the fragrance of wine. On the other hand, the sapid qualities of wine are mostly influenced by the few substances which occur in concentrations of greater than 100 milligrams per liter. They consist mostly of water, ethyl alcohol, organic acids, sugar, and glycerol and are of obvious importance.

Typical Estimates of Gross Composition (% weight) of Wines

	white	red
water	87	10
ethanol	87	10
other volatiles	0.04	0.04
extract	2.6	2.7
sugars	0.05	0.04
pectins	0.3	0.3
glycerol	1.1	1.1
acids	0.7	0.6
ash	0.2	0.2
phenols	0.01	0.2
amino acids	0.23	0.25
fats, terpenoids	0.01	0.02
vitamins, etc	0.01	0.01
total	100	100

Wine as a Biological Fluid: J of Clinical Laboratory
Analysis. 11 (1997)

Grape to Wine Chemistry

The chemical conversion of grapes into wine is an intriguing blend of both biology and chemistry and is a major transformation for some substances and only a slight transformation for other substances found in the original grapes. But the total changes are certainly noteworthy since there sure is a big difference in drinking grape juice and drinking wine! So it certainly would be worthwhile to examine some of these reactions and make the total chemistry of grapes to wine much more readily apparent.

Sugars

Most grapes contain approximately equal amounts of the common sugars glucose and fructose which are slowly produced by grape plants through photosynthesis. Fortunately, yeast can metabolize both of these sugars into ethyl alcohol which once again is good old yeast waste. This is why home winemakers usually add table sugar (sucrose) to what are often low sugar grape musts since sucrose contains equal amounts of glucose and fructose molecules. Yeast, given enough time, usually breakdown all of the glucose and fructose but even dry wines contain residual amounts of some unfermented sugars such as arabinose, rhamnose, and xylose. These unusual sugars are naturally present in small amounts in grapes and yeast do not know what to do with them. They actually do not add any sweetness to the wine but they are present in the finished product none the less.

When it really comes down to it, not all of the glucose molecules found in grapes are actually metabolized into ethyl alcohol during fermentation. Instead small amounts of glucose molecules are rearranged by the yeast during fermentation and are converted into higher alcohols, fatty acid esters, and even aldehydes. These will be shortly discussed but this is certainly good for the wine since these substances offer to us many of the aromas found in finished wines.

THE TWO COMMON SUGARS OF GRAPES

GLUCOSE   FRUCTOSE

Ethyl Alcohol (Ethanol)

Wine as an alcoholic beverage has without a doubt been consumed and enjoyed for thousands of years and was even quite necessary in some parts of the world where the drinking water was contaminated. Its ability to be low in microbial contamination allowed it to be a major liquid source in many societies. But, as a logical question, is it actually necessary for wine to have ethyl alcohol in it? Could we really produce a nonalcoholic wine that truly possesses the tastes and aromas which of course are very important in the finished product? Well, the answer is really no since ethyl alcohol plays a very complex and important role in the entire process of making wines from grapes.

ETHYL ALCOHOL - A SIMPLE MOLECULE

$$H - \underset{\underset{H}{|}}{\overset{\overset{H}{|}}{C}} - \underset{\underset{H}{|}}{\overset{\overset{H}{|}}{C}} - OH$$

Why Does Wine Need Alcohol

- it is antimicrobial allowing wine yeast to dominate
- it eliminates most spoilage organisms
- it has a slightly sweet taste
- it balances acidity making the wine less sour
- it decreases the astringency of tannins
- it reduces evaporation of the pleasant volatile compounds by dissolving them in the wine
- during aging it reacts with organic compounds producing pleasant esters and influences their stability
- during aging it reacts with aldehydes producing acetals which have a nutty taste
- it aides in extracting pigments from the grapes
- it influences the metabolic activity of yeasts thereby increasing the production of pleasant aromatics

Fixed and Volatile Acids

Grapes contain a number of fixed acids which readily do not breakdown in the wine nor do they tend to evaporate away. By far and away the two most common acids in grapes are tartaric and malic acids which as previouly shown, highly influence the pH of the fermenting must and ultimately the wine. The other three are fixed acids normally only found in very small amounts (unless malolactic fermentation occurs) and so actually have little influence on the wine.

Acid Quantity
Type (grams/liter)
Tartaric 1—5
Malic 1—4
Succinic 0.4—1
Lactic 0.1—0.4
Citric 0.04—0.7

Typical Fixed Acids

Besides influencing pH, the fixed acids are antimicrobial, precipitate pectins and proteins, and positively aid in the refreshing taste of wine. Too low of a concentration of fixed acids and the wine tastes flat like soda pop left out too long. So what we should strive for is having a fixed acid concentration in whites between .7—.8 grams per 100 milliliters and in reds around .6—.7 which is usually a wonderful balance. We shall soon see how that can easily be accomplished with sound chemistry concepts.

Grapes also contain an extremely small amount of a volatile acid (which easily evaporates and reacts with other molecules) known as acetic acid. This is the well known acid of vinegar but in the normal small amounts produced, 0.1—0.3 grams per liter, it actually adds to the desired complexity of wine. At these typical concentrations, it readily combines with other substances forming fruity esters such as ethyl acetate (general fruitiness), isoamyl acetate (banana), and benzyl acetate (apples). Only at higher concentrations does it add a vinegar aspect to the wine and this we certainly want to avoid at all costs.

Fusel Oils

Ask an organic chemist about fusel oils (higher alcohols) and the response will probably be fingers tightly squeezing the nose shut. Most of the fusel oils have a very strong disagreeable odor when concentrated, yet they can actually add to the fragrant complexities of wine in the very small amounts typically found in wine. Many home winemakers in thinking of the word alcohol are only aware of the existence of ethyl alcohol. But actually many different kinds of alcohol molecules exist in the world of chemistry and fusel oils are just big alcohol molecules. The common chemical characteristics of all alcohols is that they all contain carbon, hydrogen, and oxygen, and have attached to them an OH (hydroxyl) group as shown with the ethyl alcohol example on an earlier page. The fusel oils are structurally larger than ethyl alcohol and they contain more than two carbon atoms and grapes normally only produce them in small amounts. They are typically big named ones such as benzyl alcohol, 2-phenylethanol, 3-octanol, 1-octen-3-ol, and the herbaceous smelling 2-ethyl-hexanol. Don't worry about these weird names too much but it is nice to at least look at a couple of common examples to at least get a visible appreciation of what they look like.

TYPICAL EXAMPLES OF FUSEL OILS

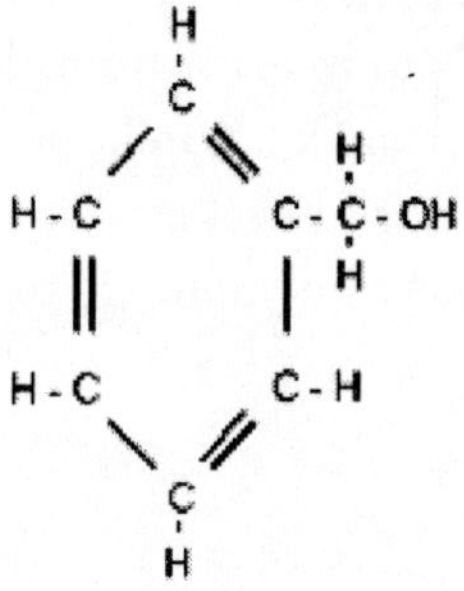

BENZYL
ALCOHOL

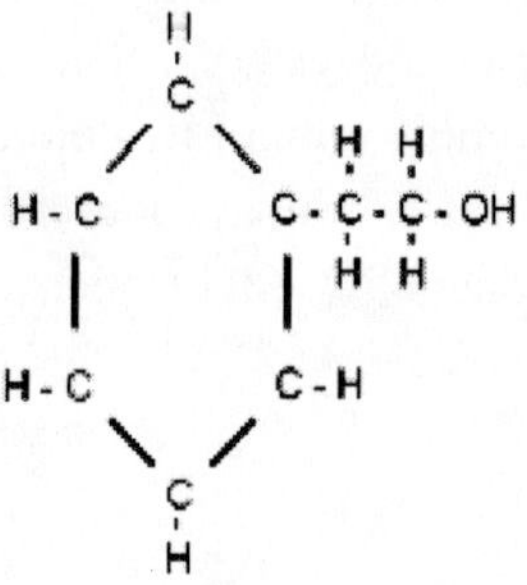

2-PHENYLETHANOL

The above substances are produced by the grapes themselves but in order to complicate matters yeast during fermentation, also produce fusel oils from reactions with sugars and amino acids. The major ones produced are 1-propanol, isobutyl alcohol, 2-methyl-1-butanol, isoamyl alcohol, and the most important 2-phenylethanol which has a distinct rose odor. Space negates the ability to draw all of their formulas (see them on the internet if you want) but they too are essentially just carbon, hydrogen, and oxygen containing compounds. What is very important to realize in regards to them is that all of these fusel oils make up about 50% of the total aromatics found in wine. Unfortunately, they occasionally can also be a problem. Fermenting under the conditions of a high temperature, high oxygen, high solids, and high pH levels can cause them to become too concentrated actually producing overwhelming pungent odors in the wine.

Esters

One of the delights one may experience through the nose is smelling the many different esters produced by many fruiting plants. Grapes naturally produce them with probably the best known ester smell of grapes coming from the Concord grape which is famous for its juices and jellies. Its well known taste and odor is mostly due to the ester methyl anthranilate which as is often in the world of chemistry some strange sounding name. But actually it is not really all that complicated since it is only made from the combination of two molecules, methyl alcohol and anthranilic acid. Since it contains a cyclic benzene structure, it is known as a cyclic (phenolic) ester which makes it perhaps just a bit more complicated.

THE WELL KNOWN CONCORD GRAPE ESTER

Actually most of the esters of wine do not come from the actual grape but are produced by yeast after fermentation has ceased and are mostly made from the combination of an alcohol and a straight chained acid such as acetic or slightly longer fatty acid chains such as hexanoic, octanoic, and decanoic. These esters can easily be made since yeast synthesize small amounts of acetic acid and the other fatty acids are available for chemical reactions in the must after being liberated by dying yeast cells. These organic acids then just slowly combine in the must with ethyl alcohol forming the following typical esters.

Common Esters in Wine
ethyl acetate—pleasant in small concentrations
isoamyl acetate—banana
benzyl acetate—apple
2-phenyl acetate—fruity
hexyl acetate—fruity
ethyl hexanoate—fruity
ethyl octanoate—fruity
ethyl decanoate—fruity

Collectively, all of these esters are only found in fairly small amounts in wine but fortunately they have a very low sensory threshold and so as a group most definitely contribute to the overall odors and complexities of most wines. The fruity esters are actually quite chemically important since they are produced early in the must and will slowly revert back to their parent organic acids and alcohol if the wine ages too long. This is the main reason why most fruity, grape wines are consumed early since with too much aging they lose much of their enjoyable fruity character.

Glycerol

Glycerol ($C_3H_8O_3$) is a slightly sweet tasting substance found in small concentrations in grapes. It is actually sort of like a small sugar molecule! Actually during active fermentation, yeast are able to synthesize more of it from an intermediate product formed from the breakdown of glucose. Fermenting at a rather high temperature increases glycerol production but even still the amount produced is relatively low. Many enologists feel that glycerol is very important in wine as it reduces a high acid wine making it less astringent and more full bodied. Unfortunately though, the normal amount of glycerol produced by grapes and even during fermentation is not really enough to by itself moderate the high acidity found in some wines. So, as will be shown later, the addition of glycerol after fermentation has ceased is highly recommended to help achieve the overall desired taste and complexity for many wines.

Methyl Alcohol and Pectins

All living organisms must produce some sort of structural material which acts somewhat like a cement in keeping their cells together and in the case of plants this cement is known as pectins. These substances are made by rearranging sugars into long chains and are commonly used to make jelly harden. To winemakers, it is important to know that pectins also possess attached to them what is called a methyl group (CH_3) which can be liberated in the must and made into small amounts of methyl alcohol. Many fruits are classically high in pectins and grapes, although not loaded with them, still contain considerable amounts. These pectins unfortunately can cause haze in wine so later on we will examine how to avoid this potential problem. But what is also interesting as just mentioned is that when the grapes are crushed to make wine musts, natural pectinase enzymes breakdown the pectins liberating the methyl group which can form methyl alcohol. Now, it is well known that methyl alcohol can be a deadly poison killing some people who have consumed as little as 30 milliliters of the stuff. But don't worry, most wines contain less methyl alcohol than other alcoholic beverages and it is totally impossible to make strong amounts of methyl alcohol as a home winemaker. Only the moon-shiner making distilled corn liquor has the ability to do that in high amounts. Actually, on a positive note, pleasant esters can be made from American grapes using chemical reactions with methyl alcohol. So, all in all, the home winemaker does not need to worry about methyl alcohol in one's wine.

Nitrogen Compounds

Grape plants, just like most other plants, absorb nitrogen compounds from the soil, in the form of ammonia (NH_3), nitrites (NO_2^-), and nitrates (NO_3^-), and combine the nitrogen with modified sugar substances to form various amino acids. These amino acids then link together to form the proteins which make up many of the structures of leaves, stems, roots, and fruits of the plant. The proteins in the fruit of grapes ultimately represents the total nitrogen content of grape musts which will be used by the yeast in making their own amino acids so they can grow and divide and then do all of the good things they do in their job of making wine.

COMMON AMINO ACIDS FOUND IN GRAPES

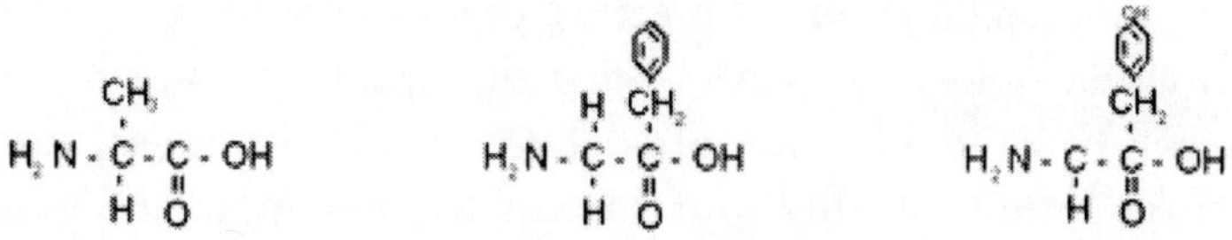

CH₃
H₂N - C - C - OH
H   O

ALANINE

H CH₂
H₂N - C - C - OH
H   O

PHENYLALANINE

CH₂
H₂N - C - C - OH
H   O

TYROSINE

Besides amino acids, some of the nitrogen compounds also rearrange themselves into histamine and phenethylamine molecules which as will be shown later cause headaches and stuffiness in a very small number of individuals. Fortunately they are only produced in moderate amounts in most wines and only a few individuals as just stated are affected by them.

Aromatic Compounds

Open a bottle of wine, pour a glass, and then gently smell the array of odors being released into the air. Wine is full of complicated amounts of several hundred different types of aromatic compounds which are unique to every type of wine. But, according to an excellent Russian study by Avakyants in 1981, the basic odor of the vast majority of wines is actually due to only seven compounds.

The Common Aromatics Found in Wine

ethyl acetate—a fruity ester in low concentrations
isoamyl acetate—creates banana or pear odors
ethyl caproate—a general fruity odor
ethyl caprylate—a pineapple odor
isobutyl alcohol—a general fruity odor
isoamyl alcohol—a general fruity odor in low concentrations
acetaldehyde—nutty in small concentrations

-IRIO

Now one might say that their wine does not smell at all like say a pineapple and this is because luckily all of these aromatic compounds tend to blend together producing a hard to define fruity odor typical to wines. What then really gives each wine its own truly unique odors are due to some of the other chemical compounds already found naturally present in the grape varieties. For example, the extremely popular Cabernet Sauvignon and some Sauvignon blanc wines have a bell pepper odor attributed to a hard to pronounce compound called 2-methoxy-3-isobutylpryrazine. It can easily be drawn but should we really bother since its just neat being able to pronounce it! An even better known odor is the so called "foxy" smell found in many American VITIS LABRUSCA grapes such as Concord and Niagara. These odors are attributed to the already discussed methyl anthranilate ester but also to ethyl-3-mercaptopropionate, furaneol, and damascenone molecules. Many readily enjoy this foxy aroma and some very excellent sparkling wines have been produced from these grapes in cold weather climates.

Another group of grapes are noted for their highly unusual flowery and fruity odors. These are the Muscats and a group of German grapes notably Riesling and Gewurtztraminer. These varieties contain substantial amounts of monoterpenes which can exist free, as an alcohol, an oxide, or even bound to sugars (glycosides). These highly odiferous substances have been described as spicy and even iris-like and are found in both the skin and juice of these wonderful grapes which are esteemed by many worldwide.

The Main Monoterpenes of German Grapes

linalool—an orange flower aroma
gerianol—a rose-like odor
nerol—a sweet rose-like odor
citronellol—an oily lemon odor
alpha-terpineol—a pine-like odor

THOSE COMPLICATED MONOTERPENE MOLECULES

LINALOOL
(ORANGE FLOWER)

GERIANOL
(ROSE)

Other substances also exist in these German grapes and wines including vanillan (vanilla-like), methyl vanillate, zingerone, coniferyl alcohol, and 4-vinylguaiacol. Most of these substances are mainly found in white German grapes and only a few in red German grapes. Most of these German wines are not aged for long periods of time since the monoterpenes slowly combine with small amounts of oxygen forming monoterpene oxides which then tend to lose their floral smells. For example, a typical young Riesling wine may contain around 400 micrograms per liter of various monoterpenes but after three years of aging may decline to less than 100 micrograms per liter which is below the odor detection level and makes the wine much less floral.

Few other white wine varieties possess these highly scented monoterpenes. In fact, overall the odor in most white wines is mainly attributed to the fatty acid esters ethyl caproate, ethyl caprate, and ethyl laurate which have as already been shown possess fruity characteristics of their own. Collectively these esters are generally present at the small levels of less than 10 milligrams per liter but this is actually ten times higher than their detection levels and so are highly fruity in the long run.

Anthocyanins and Tannins (Phenolics)

Now it is time to really get down to some truly interesting wine chemistry. Of all of the reactions changing grapes into wine, none are more complicated than the chemical changes which occur to the phenols and pigments found in the grape. These phenolic substances affect the color, fragrance, mouth-fell, appearance, astringency, bitterness, flatness, and antimicrobial aspects of the resulting wine so they must be pretty important in the overall winemaking process.

What Actually Are These Phenolics

As previously shown, phenolics are actually substances based on the structure of benzene with an OH group attached to it. In grapes and wine, they combine and form interesting benzene derived substances such as anthocyanins and tannins. Most people are aware of at least the taste of tannins. All one has to do is to let dark tea seep in hot water too long and the strong, bitter, astringent tastes of tannins are readily apparent. Red wine is often high in tannins but red grapes themselves do not contain much of them so it must be in the transformation of grapes into wine that tannins are really produced. In fact, all kinds of phenolic substances are transformed in the process of making wine and some are even produced by the yeast themselves. Actually the only real phenol produced by yeast in small amounts is known as tyrosol which is made by yeast from the amino acid tyrosine. Wine stored in oak also contains slightly more tyrosol but still this is only a minor phenol in wine. On the other hand, the main phenolics in wine come from grape skins, seeds, and juices and are classified in the world of chemistry as either flavonoids or nonflavonoids.

Flavonoids

Flavonoids are phenolic substances that are categorized as either flavonols, catechins, anthocyanins, or leucoanthocyanins. Once again here we have more crazy chemistry words to knock into our brains! What they all have in common is a structure known as the aglycone which consists of two phenolic aromatic rings joined in between by a pyran (6 carbon) ring which contains an oxygen atom.

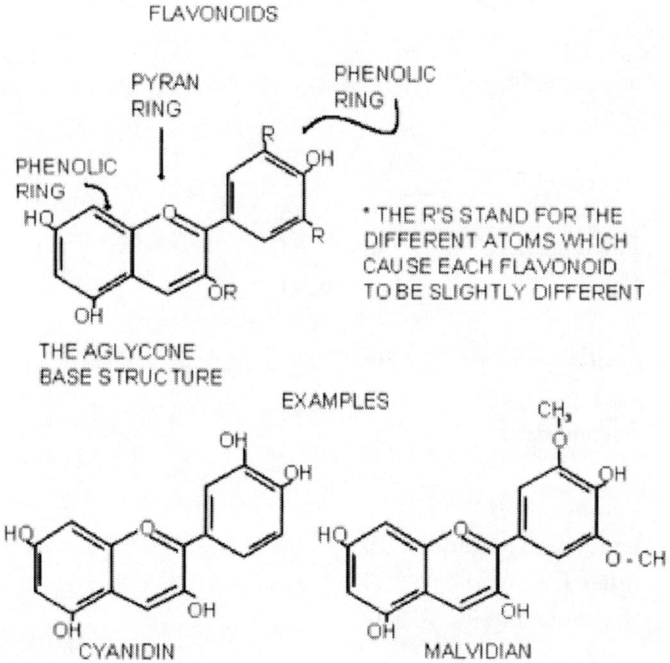

FLAVONOIDS

PYRAN RING

PHENOLIC RING

PHENOLIC RING

* THE R'S STAND FOR THE DIFFERENT ATOMS WHICH CAUSE EACH FLAVONOID TO BE SLIGHTLY DIFFERENT

THE AGLYCONE BASE STRUCTURE

EXAMPLES

CYANIDIN

MALVIDIAN

Some of the flavonoids exist in a truly free state but the majority are actually more complicated as they are attached to a sugar, polymerized to either other flavonoids or nonflavonoids.

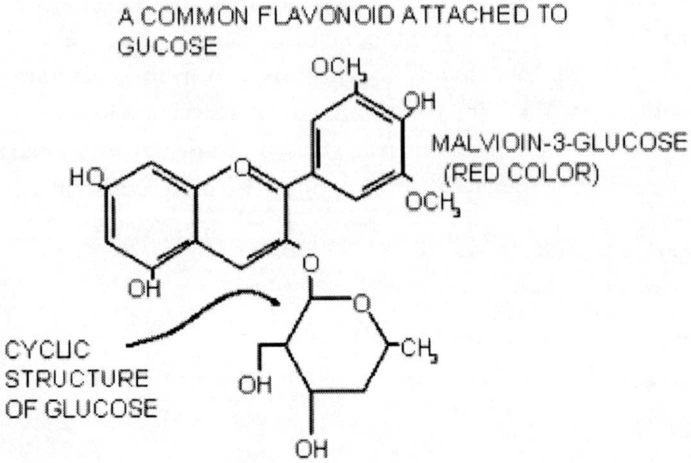

A COMMON FLAVONOID ATTACHED TO
GUCOSE
OCH3
OH
MALVIOIN-3-GLUCOSE
(RED COLOR)
HO
O
OCH3
O
OH
O
CYCLIC
STRUCTURE
OF GLUCOSE
CH3
OH
OH

Phenolic Levels in a "typical" VITIS VINIFERA Red Wine

Phenol Type	Conc mg/L
nonflavonoids	200
flavonoids	
anthocyanins	150
condensed tannins	750
other flavonoids	250
flavonols	50

Nonflavonoids

Grapes also contain nonflavonoids derived from the grape juice mostly in the form of hydroxycinnamic and hydroxybenzoic acids. Both red and white grapes contain pretty much the same amount of these substances and they are usually chemically attracted to sugars, organic acids and alcohol. If oak is used during fermentation or aging, polymers (long chains) of ellagic acid and gallic acid are liberated from the wood and the wood lignin also provides cinnamaldehyde and benzaldehyde substances to the wine.

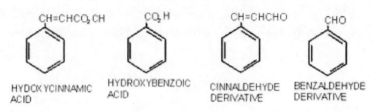

Tannins

Most people are probably aware that wine varieties contain differing levels of tannins. What might not be known chemistry wise is that the tannins are made up of flavonoids and nonflavonoids which link together forming long molecular chains known as polymers. Actually the simplified generic term for a tannin is any substance that can tan leather! Hawley's Condensed Chemical dictionary more specifically defines a tannin as "any broad group of plant-derived phenolic compounds characterized by their ability to precipitate proteins". This is the chemical definition that home winemakers should understand and appreciate. To go into more detailed chemistry, nonflavonoids are really known as hydrolyzable tannins, since under the acidic conditions found in wine, they breakdown (hydrolyze) into smaller components which tend to remain in the wine and so they can easily add to harshness and bitterness if found in excess. The flavonoid components found in grapes and wine are different in that they do not break apart in the acid conditions of wine. In fact, the opposite occurs as wine ferments and ages. The flavonoids actually connect together with each other forming larger molecular structures known as polymers. What actually happens is that the catechin flavonoids readily combine with each other during fermentation forming what we call procyanidins and they usually consist of 2—5 subunits in length. Then rather slowly with aging, these procyanidin complexes attach to each other forming what we call condensed tannins. They tend to be 8—14 subunits in length and many of them slowly sink to the bottom of the must where they can be removed by racking thereby lowering the astringency and bitterness of the wine.

A CONDENSED TANNIN

Tannins Precipitate Proteins

A certain amount of tannins are actually good for the home winemaker and this is especially true for those making red wines. As noted, proteins in wine must often cause a haze in wines which can be quite difficult to clear. Here is where tannins can come to the rescue since they will easily attach themselves to proteins in the must and literally sink them to the bottom where they can be removed by racking. This is great for red wines which often contain lots of tannins and so precipitating tannin-protein complexes actually removes two potential problems. We shall also soon see that other ways are available for removing the protein haze in whites since they contain little in the way of tannins and so do not naturally form these dense complexes.

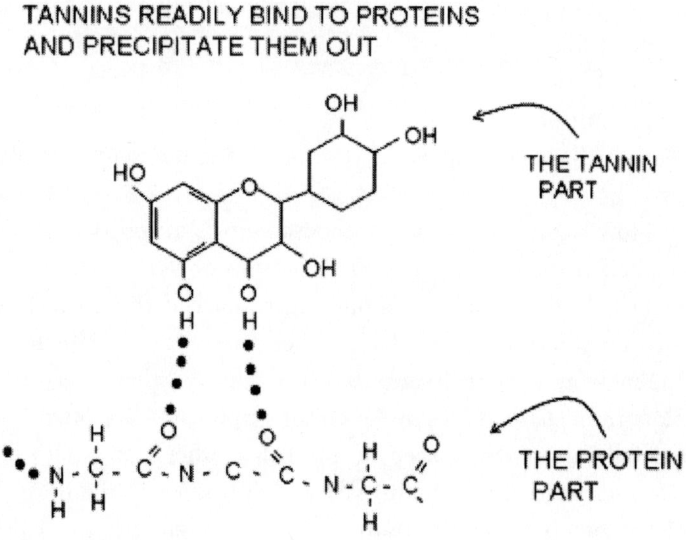

**TANNINS READILY BIND TO PROTEINS
AND PRECIPITATE THEM OUT**

THE TANNIN PART

THE PROTEIN PART

The Pigment Containing Anthocyanins Which Make Wine Colorful

By now one might be saying that the chemistry involved with the phenolics of grapes is pretty complicated and yet we still have not even looked at the pigment containing phenolics yet! These substances which make up the colors of wine are the anthocyanins and they usually exist as glucosides (anthocyanins bonded to sugars or to organic acids such as caffeic, acetic, or coumaric). Luckily for enologists these complexes are soluble, stable, and resist oxidation so colors are usually retained for a long time in wine.

The Five Classes of Anthocyanins

cyanidin—the substance from which all others are formed
peodinin
delphinidin
petunidin
malvidian—major one in VINIFERA and is the reddest of all

How many sugars each anthocyanidin is attached to depends on whether the juice is from VITIS VINIFERA or VITIS LABRUSCA since the French grapes only have one sugar attached (monoglucosides) and the American grapes have either one or two (diglucosides). One may say who really cares but it is actually easier to extract the colors from diglucosides so American grape wines are often highly colorful! But certainly keep in mind that other factors also influence color intensity including pH and SO_2 levels in the must. The role of pH is very important since these pigments can exist in solutions in different forms ranging from colorless to pale yellow and from blue violet to red. In red musts at a pH less than 4, the main color in the wine is red but as pH rises, more blue violet colors dominate. SO_2 additions during early fermentation also can affect anthocyanin color pigmentation since too much SO_2 can actually bleach these pigments by combining with them. Usually this is only a temporary condition.

EXCESSIVE AMOUNTS OF SO_2 MAY BLEACH PIGMENTS

COLORED MALVIDIAN IONS BINDS WITH BISULFITE (SO_2)

FORMS A COLORLESS MALVIDIAN SULFATE

COLORLESS

Actually when to first add SO_2 is constantly being argued by enologists since many feel that in the case of red musts it really should not be initially added so that bleaching does not occur even though this condition is once again only temporary. But also too much early SO_2 additions can cause the early extraction of high amounts of catechins which may increase bitterness in the ultimate wine. It can also slow down the rate of copigmentation which will soon be discussed. But on the other hand, early SO_2 additions do destroy unwanted microorganisms so probably the best bet is to just add minimal amounts of SO_2 initially to red musts. Of course, as we shall see it is quite important to add SO_2 initially to white wine musts to prevent oxidation reactions from occurring during early fermentation.

Copigmentation

Copigmentation is a relatively new wine term which refers to the binding of anthocyanins to tannins. It is very important that copigmentation occurs in red wines so that these so called co-polymers are retained in solution in the wine thereby retaining the colors of the pigment. Unfortunately, anthocyanin pigments not polymerized to tannins are easily oxidized by both oxygen and SO_2. Oxidation itself is a well known chemistry term that refers to the ripping off of electrons from some sort of chemical substance. If a substance such as oxygen rips electrons from another chemical substance, we say that that substance has been oxidized. This is indeed what may happen to certain anthocyanin pigments if exposed to too much oxygen and the results are often bad color changes in the wine. So, hopefully by the end of fermentation, 25% of the anthocyanin pigments will be polymerized to tannins, 40% at one year of aging, and 100% by three years of aging. With more aging of red wines, it is naturally true that the red pigments will take on a more yellow brown color but they will also be less astringent which is one of the benefits of aging hearty red wines. Another interesting aspect of aging is that we can actually get a more rapid binding of the anthocyanin pigments to tannins if the young wines are exposed to a small amount of oxygen at bottling which usually happens anyway. This minute amount of oxygen causes small amounts of ethyl alcohol to oxidize into acetaldehyde and this substance can actually reverse the bleaching of the pigments by SO_2. The acetaldehyde also then forms actual polymers with the pigment—tannin complexes which also makes them more stable. Also adding back small amounts of sugar after fermentation has ceased aides in color retention since the sugars also bind to these soluble complexes making them even more attracted to the water in the wine and so they are even more soluble and therefore colors are retained much longer.

White Wine and Phenols

The role that phenolics play in white wine production is much different than that found in red wines since white grapes are naturally very low in colored pigments. Instead, most of the phenolics in white grapes consist of the nonflavonoids caftaric acid (caffeoyl tartaric acid), p-coumaric acid, and ferulic acid. These nonflavonoids do help to give overall body to the wine but they can readily be oxidized by oxygen causing them to turn into nasty brown pigments and nobody wants a brown, white wine! Adding SO_2 initially to white wine musts is highly advised since it slows down this oxidation since the SO_2 interferes with the ability of oxygen to do its nasty oxidative business and so this is a common practice to winemakers.

Resveratrol

For the time being, let's leave the complicated chemistry of phenolics and instead examine another easy to understand phenol known as resveratrol. Known as 3,5,4-trihydroxystilibene this exciting molecule is now being stressed by medical science as a truly healthy substance when taken into the human body.

Resveratrol is produced by certain grapes in order to inhibit the growth of molds which commonly afflict many grapes while they are growing. The amount produced by each variety varies but we might as well make up some generalities. For one, most white grapes only contain about 1—5% of the amounts of resveratrol found in red grapes. We also know that many of the red grapes grown in warm climates contain low amounts of it but that is not always true since many Italian wines contain substantial amounts. On the other hand, red American grapes grown in cold climates tend to have higher amounts of resveratrol and even white Rieslings contain adequate amounts. Processing may also affect its concentrations since aging in oak may reduce its amounts by up to 68%.

Finally, we are also aware that filtering the wine may cause substantial loses of this very important substance.

Hopefully in years to come commercial enologists will label
the concentrations of resveratrol in their wines since many wine
drinkers are also quite health conscious and it is really only found
in a few other foods such as peanuts and mulberries.

RESVERATROL

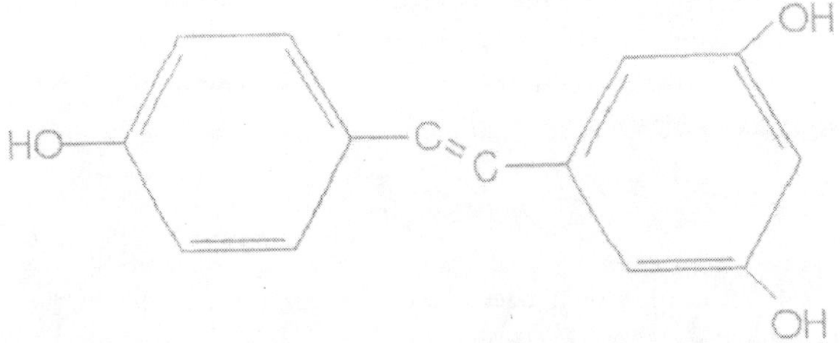

HO⟶⟨⟩⟶C=C⟶⟨⟩⟶OH

OH

The Health Benefits of Resveratrol

• acts as an antioxidant (like the well known vitamins C and E)
  neutralizing poisonous free radicals—less heart disease and
  cancer
• lessens LDL synthesis (bad cholesterol)—less heart disease
• raises HDL levels (good cholesterol)—less heart disease
• reduces inflammation in arteries—less heart disease
• reduces the clumping of platelets—less heart attacks and
  strokes
• helps to inactivate enzymes in the liver which can actually
  activate free radical poisons—less cancer

- protects polyunsaturated fatty acids from being damaged by free radicals
- may inhibit androgen—stimulated cell growth in the prostate by inhibiting the androgen receptor—less prostate cancer
- actually has been found to capture formaldehyde (which is naturally produced in our body) and eliminate this poison

CHAPTER 3. THE WINEMAKING PROCESS

"Fermentation is correlative with life. Wine is the most healthful and most hygienic of all beverages." Louis Pasteur

Being a home winemaker can be considered an art since it takes skill, patience, education, and practice. But what is chemically interesting is that the general process is similar whether we are making reds, whites, or even fruity wines. Of course, differences do exist but that is one of the enjoyments of being able to adjust to the variables depending on what variety is being fermented. But essentially what we all strive for is sound grapes, careful measurements, good sterilization techniques, close observations and of course patience.

Sterilization

Everybody inhales bacteria, fungi, and even wild yeast with every breath we take since these microorganisms are literally floating about everywhere. So it is also very easy for them to land into glass carboys, other fermentation vessels, and just about any other piece of equipment used by home winemakers. Even if all of the equipment is dry, these organisms can remain inactive and quite viable for long periods of time. When we add juices (musts) and begin fermentation, these wild organisms wake up, start to grow, and may contaminate the musts with many off-odors. So, it is quite apparent that we must seek as sterile of an environment as possible to limit these critters and fortunately a wide array of cleaners are available to us.

Common Sterilizing and Cleaning Agents

- potassium or sodium metabisufite—for sterilizing bottles etc—
  it becomes SO_2 gas which kills microbes citric acid—a 5%
  solution is a good sterilizer and a 1% solution removes paper
  taste from filters
- soda ash—Na_2CO_3—cleans and sanitizes glass and barrels—
  removes tartrate deposits and also labels from bottles
- chlorine bleach a strong oxidant which kills microbes but must
  be washed out completely or it may react to produce off-
  odors in corked wine
- iodine sold as iodine + a nonionic wetting agent called io-
  dophor—does not clean equipment but kills microbes
- detergent works best to remove organic matter on equipment
  but really does not sanitize
- chlorinated trisodium phosphate—probably the best of all
  since it removes organic matter from equipment and also
  destroys microbes

The amount of each cleaner and sanitizer to use can be easily
be found but the main concept to remember is to make sure to
completely wash all of the equipment thoroughly with water so
that none of these substances are left as they may contribute to
problems later in the wine.

Adding the Grapes

The actual selection of what type of grape variety to buy is of
course personal choice but usually fresh or frozen juices are prefer-
able to concentrates. Hopefully, whatever is chosen will be made
from high quality varietal grapes and so it is always wise to know
the supplier. Most vineyards will be happy to explain all of the
specifics of this years harvest and that can go a long way in aiding
the ultimate outcome of the winemaking adventure.

Pectic Enzymes

Pectins are great if one is a jelly maker, but they can form haziness in wines and most fruits are loaded with them. Although not as high in pectins as most fruits, grapes still contain a substantial amount of them. Pectins, are related to carbohydrates and consist of long chains of galacturonic acid (pectinic acid) units bonded together. Pectins are combined with plant cellulose and makeup the cell walls of many of the cells in fruits. When grapes are crushed into juice, the pectins, which are highly polar, stay in solution in the must. As a result, these long molecular substances will cause haze and reduce the clarity of wine if they are not broken apart. So, what the winemaker needs to do is to add commercially prepared pectic enzymes to the juice must at the beginning of fermentation. These enzymes are extracted from the common mold ASPERGILLUS and contain differing concentrations of the pectic enzymes pectin methyl esterase, pectin lyase, pectin transliminase, and polygalaturonase. When added to the must, these pectic enzymes attack the pectins in differing areas and break them down into much smaller particles which can then settle to the bottom of the must. There they can ultimately be removed by racking and we end up with a clear wine.

This process is very important since it will result in a more rapid flow of juice, greater clarity, more pronounced colors, and even a better flavor. Also in the case of LABRUSCA and French hybrid juices the addition of these enzymes will result in the production of more methyl esters. Typical preparations call for the addition of 3 drops per gallon for grapes and 10 drops for other fruits. Many home winemakers actually add 4—8 drops per gallon for VINIFERA and hybrids, 10—14 per gallon for LABRUSCA, and 20—28 per gallon for fruits with very good results.

Sugar Addition

An interesting botanical question is why in the world are fruits such as grapes loaded with sugar. Well of course the answer is that plants through photosynthesis are able to make large amounts of glucose and lots of it is used immediately as an energy source. But plants make more glucose than what they need for their energy requirements and some of it is converted into a very sweet tasting sugar compound named fructose. A good bit of the glucose and fructose is then sent into the developing fruits which also contain grape seeds. Fruit such as grapes are very sweet so that animals eat them and the seeds then pass out of their digestive system where they ultimately germinate in soil. So, this aides in dispersing the seeds in different areas which is one of nature's ways insuring the survival of a plant species.

The Sugars in Grapes

All grape varieties contain differing amounts of sugars and typically those produced in warm climates such as California generally produce high levels of sugars. Conversely, grapes grown in cold climates are much lower in their total sugar content. This is important information for the home winemaker since a certain amount of sugar has to be in grape juice (must) in order for the yeast to be able to produce an alcohol content of at least 10% so that the wine becomes stable and preserves well. Many wines with an alcohol content below 10% must be consumed very early since a low alcohol content produces a very unstable wine. So, most home winemakers strive to produce a wine with an alcohol content between 10 and 12% and this can be easily accomplished using simple chemical analysis of the sugar content.

The Hydrometer

A hydrometer is a simple devise which measures the specific gravity of wine juice. One can also purchase one that also measures sugar content and potential alcohol. It consists of a hollow cylindrical glass tube weighed at the bottom with steel shot with specific graduations and is an important chemical instrument to the home winemaker.

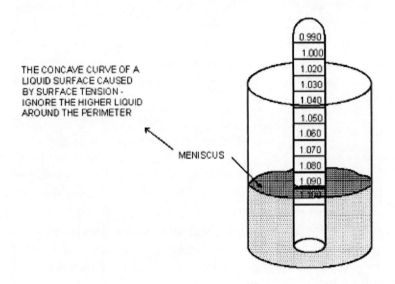

THE CONCAVE CURVE OF A
LIQUID SURFACE CAUSED
BY SURFACE TENSION -
IGNORE THE HIGHER LIQUID
AROUND THE PERIMETER

MENISCUS

0.990
1.000
1.020
1.030
1.040
1.050
1.060
1.070
1.080
1.090

The real chemical question though is what is specific gravity all about? In the precise world of chemistry it is a measurement of the weight (gravity) of a liquid in relation to the weight of water. Since the relationship of gravity to water is specified, the ultimate measurement is simply known as specific gravity. Chemists are well aware that if we drop a hydrometer into plain old pure water, the specific gravity measurement will read 1.000 on the hydrometer. But, grape juice besides containing water, also contains some sugar solids so putting a hydrometer in this juice will cause it to float higher giving a reading above 1.000. On the other hand, if we put a hydrometer into pure ethyl alcohol, the hydrometer should actually read 0.792 since its specific gravity is less than water.. So to put things into perspective, if we start to ferment sugar containing grape must, and ferment it to dryness, we should end up with wine that basically contains water and alcohol and so the final reading should be around 0.990. Don't worry about all those other neat little ingredients in the wine since they have little influence on the ultimate specific gravity measurements. So, what specific gravity measurement should we start out with if we wish to ferment a must to 12% alcohol? Well, chemists know that theoretically 17 grams of sugar will yield 10 grams of ethyl alcohol. So by doing some mathematics, we have found that if we start with a specific gravity reading of 1.090, and ferment the must to dryness, we should end up with a wine containing around 12% alcohol. If more or less alcohol is desired, the following chart can be utilized. It is based on wine must at 15.5°C (60°F) so if the temperature of the must is different then a slight calculation adjustment must be used.

Initial Specific Gravity	Potential Alcohol	Temperature Adjustment		
		°C	°F	Correction
1.075	10.4	10	50	0.005
1.080	11.1	15.5	60	0.000
1.085	11.9	21	70	+0.001
1.090	12.7	25	77	+0.002
1.095	13.1	29	84	+0.003
1.100	14.2	35	95	+0.005

Brix Scale

Another scale common to hydrometers is known as the Brix scale named after its inventor Adolf Brix. This scale is really easier to use than specific gravity since it just measures the suspended solids in must which are just mostly sugar molecules. Ounces per gallon are the basis of this scale and a Brix reading of 23.1 (23.1% sugar) equals a specific gravity of 1.095. Therefore, if one starts with an initial Brix reading of 23.1, the final ethyl alcohol concentration should also be around 12%—13%.

Brix and Ethyl Alcohol Concentrations

Brix	Potential Alcohol
18.7	10.4
18.8	11.1
20.9	11.9
22.0	12.7
23.1	13.1
24.2	14.2
25.3	15.0

Chaptalization Or The Addition of Sugar

Every year is different in regards to the amount of natural sugars found in every variety of grape. As a result one should always take a specific gravity or Brix reading to determine how much sugar is in the initial must. If it is too low, then one can chaptilize (started by Dr Chaptal in 1801) which is nothing more than adding sugar to the must to reach the desired sugar concentration. Reaching the levels is quite easy by measuring out the sugar in cups.

Chaptalization Conversion Table

2 cups sugar = 1 pound sugar = 454 grams sugar
1 cup sugar = .5 pounds sugar = 227 grams sugar
¾ cup sugar = .375 pounds sugar = 170 grams sugar
½ cup sugar = .25 pounds sugar = 113.5 grams sugar
¼ cup sugar = .125 pounds = 56.75 grams sugar

We can raise the Brix by a factor of 1 by adding .1 pounds of sugar per gallon of must. So, for example if the initial Brix is 19 and we wish to go to a Brix of 23, calculate the following:

23 minus 19 = 4 then 4 x .1 = .4 so add .4 pounds of sugar per gallon which is slightly more than ¾ of a cup

Many home winemakers make 5 gallons of wine at a time so here would be the calculations used for this common amount of wine.

23 minus 19 = 4 then 4 x .5 = 2.0 so add 4 cups of sugar to 5 gallons of must

Many home winemakers like to use concentrates and these are very low in sugar since the concentrates are added to lots of water to achieve 5 gallons of must. After adding the concentrate to water, the Brix level may be as low as 5 so obviously lots of sugar must be added. For example, 23 minus 5 = 18 then 18 x .5 = 9 pounds of sugar which means 18 cups of sugar must be added to the must. Luckily table sugar is still one of the cheaper substances available at the supermarket.

Acid Adjustments

Now it is time to check out the initial acid levels of the musts since too much acid is no good and too little is even worse. As previously noted, tartaric and malic acids make up between 70—90% of the total acids in grapes and these levels vary year by year with each variety. Once again, the amount of malic acid available also varies depending on warm and cold climate grapes. How much acid is desired depends on one's preference but the acidity levels generally range between .55 to .85 grams per 100 milliliters (percent). Most enologists like a red wine to be .6—.7 and whites to be around .7—.8. Every juice or concentrate contains differing amounts, but as a general rule warm climate grapes (mostly VINIFERA) contain low amounts of acids and cold climate grapes (mostly LABRUSCA) or even hybrids contain too much acid.

Acetification of Warm Climate Grapes

If a grape must is initially low in acid one can quite easily add known concentrations of organic acids to the musts. This process known as acetification is a very common procedure and many home winemakers purchase an acid blend which is a mixture of tartaric, malic, and citric acids. But, a word of caution is that wine chemists often do not recommend these blends since both malic and citric acids may be broken down into undesirable substances such as acetic acid during the fermentation process. On the other hand, tartaric is a very stable organic acid and when added to musts actually raises the acidity and also lowers the pH which is what is usually desired. The world of mathematics once again comes into play when figuring out tartaric acid addition to musts. We find that 3.8 grams (1 teaspoon) added to one gallon will raise the acidity by .1% or 19 grams to five gallons (5 teaspoons).

Tartaric Acid Additions to Must in Grams

Gallons of Must	raise .1	raise .2	raise .3	raise .4
1.0	3.8	7.7	11.4	15.5
2.0	7.7	15.4	23.1	30.8
3.0	11.4	22.8	34.2	45.6
5.0	19.0	38.5	57.0	76

The Simple Acid Test

1. buy a test kit at a wine making store or see your local chemist friend
2. the equipment; .1 molar sodium hydroxide (a diluted strong base), phenolpthalein (a common indicator), 5 milliliter pipette, an erlenmeyer flask or beaker, a buret and buret stand, grape must
3. fill the buret with about 20 milliliters of sodium hydroxide and then fill the beaker (erlenmeyer) with 100 milliliters of hot distilled water. Then pipette 5 milliliters of grape must into the distilled water.
4. add 5 drops of the phenolpthalein indicator to the now diluted must.
5. take an initial reading of the amount of sodium hydroxide in the graduated buret and then slowly add drop by drop the sodium hydroxide into the beaker with constant swirling. The pink coloration from the indicator will quickly disappear but as you add more sodium hydroxide, the pink color will remain for longer periods of time as the base neutralizes more acid in the wine. When the pink color does not disappear quickly it is time to slow down the titration. Being very careful, just add one drop of sodium hydroxide at a time and swirl the diluted must. Do this until finally the faint pink color stays and does not disappear.

   Stop immediately since this is the endpoint where you have finally neutralized all of the acids in the must with the sodium hydroxide base.
6. Measure on the buret exactly how many milliliters of sodium hydroxide base was needed to neutralize the must acids.
7. Multiply that number by .15 and this will give you the starting acidity values in your grape must and you can then add known amounts of acids to the must if necessary.

What If My Juice Contains Too Much Acid

Once again, many cold climate grapes actually contain too much acid and so often we must actually reduce their acid levels in order for the wine to be drinkable. Many enologists actually add low acid wines (blending) to these musts to reduce acidity while others add water (amelioration) to dilute out the acids. Amelioration usually works out quite well since adding water not only dilutes the acidity but also causes more of the stable tartaric acid molecules to breakdown (dissociate giving off more H+ ions into the must which keeps the pH around the wine pH of 3.3).

The Direct Addition of Weak Bases to Musts To Lower Acidity

Some home winemakers actually add either calcium carbonate ($CaCO_3$) or potassium carbonate (K_2CO_3) to their musts to neutralize out some of the excess acids. It is just another reaction in the world of chemistry!

$$CaCo_3 + C_4H_6O_4 \rightarrow CaC_4H_4O_6 + H_2O$$

Calcium carbonate + tartaric acid $\rightarrow$ calcium tartrate + water

Now this is a very nifty chemical reaction but the potential problem is that calcium tartrate precipitates out of the must very slowly and some calcium malate may also be formed which can give wine a salty taste. But still many home winemakers think this process works quite well and 3.8 grams of calcium carbonate added per gallon will reduce acidity by .15%. If using teaspoons, 2 teaspoons per gallon reduces acidity by .1%. If one uses potassium carbonate then 3.4 grams per gallon will reduce the acidity by .15%. If one uses teaspoons, approximately 1.5 teaspoons will reduce acidity by .1% per gallon.

Potassium carbonate may actually work better since potassium tartrate crystals will form which can be removed later on through a soon to be discussed technique called Cold Stabilization.

A final note in regards to acidity is that on occasion, especially in cold weather grapes, one encounters an unusual condition of the grapes containing high acids but also a high pH. A solution to this problem is to add 2—8 milliliters per gallon of 35% phosphoric acid which is the acid typically added in small amounts to soda pop. This acid is available at winemaking outlets and will lower the pH without a significant increase in total acids.

Sulfur Dioxide

Luckily for winemakers, most microbes such as bacteria and molds have a hard time growing in the acidic conditions of fermenting grape juice. But, some tough microbes do grow at a pH less than 5 and they can really foul up the fermentations and produce some very nasty off-flavors that can spoil a lot of hard work. For thousands of years these microbes most likely made many winemakers quite unhappy and probably somewhat irritated. Then miraculously some early wine chemist found that by adding sulfur to musts and wines they were able to produce a much tastier product with less off-flavors that also preserved much better. The key inhibiting agent from the sulfur was actually sulfur dioxide (SO_2) and some ancient winemakers actually produced it by burning brimstone. In the 1500's Europeans literally burned sulfur candles directly into their barrels producing SO_2 gas. Today, almost all winemakers use controlled doses of this gas to not only inhibit undesirable microbes but also to act as an antioxidant, and also to influence the taste and sensory properties of their wines. Nothing has been found to work better even though the French Pasteur Institute has for years offered 10,000 Francs for anyone who can find a better antimicrobial agent. What also makes SO_2 desirable is that the wine yeast SACCHAROMYCES CEREVISIAE can readily tolerate the usual amounts of

SO_2 added to musts and so it soon becomes the dominant yeast species in the must. Currently the BATF (Bureau of Alcohol, Tobacco, and Firearms) allows commercial wines to contain up to 350 milligrams per liter total SO_2 which is actually much more than is really needed. Most home winemakers would do quite well only having 20—40 milligrams per liter SO_2 at bottling.

The Benefits of SO_2 Additions

1. Inhibits undesirable microorganisms
2. Reduces the oxidation of wines by inhibiting oxygen availability in musts and wine.
3. Reduces the darkening of pigments by halting the activation of grape enzymes known as tyrosinases which oxidize colorless nonflavonoids (dihydroxyphenols) in grapes into dark colored quinones.
4. Combines with tannins forming more stable complexes.
5. Aides in wine preservation.

How Can One Get SO_2 in Musts and Wine

Sulfur Dioxide exists naturally in the form of a gas and commercial winemakers can directly inject it into their musts. Most home winemakers obtain their SO_2 by directly adding the salt potassium metabisulfite ($K_2O_5S_2$) which is the potassium salt of sulfur dioxide. When this salt is placed into the acidic conditions of wine it liberates SO_2 gas and a number of other sulfur chemicals such as H_2SO_3 (sulfurous acid), HSO_3^- (bisulfite ion), and SO_3^- (sulfate ion).

$$O=S=O$$

$$SO_2$$

$$H \; O\text{-}S\text{-}O$$
$$\overset{\|}{O}$$

$$H_2SO_3$$

$$HSO_3^-$$

$$SO_3^{-2}$$

$$K_2O_5S_2 \qquad + K$$

The predominant substances liberated upon potassium metabisulfite additions are SO_2 in its molecular form and the bisulfite ion. Only the free molecular SO_2 inhibits the growth of microbes since some of the SO_2 and most of the bisulfite ions bind to acetaldehyde, anthocyanins, glucose, and even proteins. This binding is pH and temperature dependent with less binding occurring at low pHs and low temperatures. So the lower the pH and the lower the fermentation temperature will cause less SO_2 binding so more free molecular SO_2 will be available to inhibit microbes. This is great since then less potassium metabisulfite needs to be added to the must.

THE BINDING OF BISULFITE TO ACETALDEHYDE

THE SO₂ PART

$$CH_3\text{-}\overset{H}{\underset{}{C}}=O \;\; + \;\; HO\text{-}\overset{\|}{\underset{O}{S}}O \;\; \longrightarrow \;\; CH_3\text{-}\overset{H}{\underset{OH}{C}}\text{-}\overset{O}{\underset{O}{S}}O$$

ACETALDEHYDE   BISULFITE   HYDROXYSULFONATE

Actually the binding of the bisulfite ion to acetaldehyde molecules is good for the winemaker since the product produced, hydroxysulfonate is more sensory neutral than the often overpowering sense of acetaldehyde.

Total Sulfur Dioxide

Chemists like to define the amount of SO_2 in musts as what is called "Total Sulfur Dioxide" and it consists of both free molecular SO_2 and bound SO_2. Winemakers really only want to deal with the free molecular SO_2 and studies show that it generally takes 0.8 milligrams per liter free molecular SO_2 to inhibit the growth of most spoilage microbes. So for example, using a typical wine must pH of 3.4, we can achieve 0.8 by adding 32 milligrams per liter of metabisulfite to the must. Again we must add more since much of the metabisulfite forms other sulfur compounds and some of the molecular SO_2 binds to other substances in the must. Most home winemakers add SO_2 to their musts through potassium metabisulfite additions or by using the common Campden Tablets which contain pre-measured amounts of metabisulfite. These SO_2 additions are either expressed in milligrams per liter or in parts per million (ppm) which are actually the same thing. Each Campden Tablet supplies 65 mg/L (ppm) per gallon or 13 mg/L (ppm) in 5 gallons at a pH of 3.2—3.5.

Amount of Metabisulfite Addition Needed to Achieve 0.8 milligrams per liter Molecular SO_2

pH	Milligrams per Liter
3.0	13
3.1	16
3.2	21
3.3	26
3.4	32
3.5	40
3.6	50

SO$_2$ Can Get Real Complicated

Charts are nice to have around but the amount of SO$_2$ to add to musts is very much dependent on pH, yeast type, and even grape variety so as always things can be rather complicated. But lets deal with the following generalities which should put SO$_2$ in a proper perspective. For one, many home winemakers prefer not to add any, or only small amounts of SO$_2$ initially to red wine musts since the early addition of this substance can delay necessary phenol polymerization and can also bleach the pigments although this condition is only temporary. It is just the opposite for whites since SO$_2$ additions actually bleach potential brown pigments allowing for a more pleasing paler color and it also lessens oxidation reactions. It is also noteworthy that SO$_2$ levels decline as fermentation proceeds, so home winemakers often add more of it with each racking to maintain a minimal level throughout the entire fermentation. Finally, at bottling, it is essential to add enough SO$_2$ to age the wine correctly and preserve it. So most home winemakers routinely add 20—40 milligrams per liter right before bottling which should then give a free molecular SO$_2$ concentration of between 0.5 and 0.9 if the pH is between the desired 3.1—3.5 levels.

Mathematical Calculations

As previously noted, Campden Tablets are available at winemaking stores and each tablet supplies 65 milligrams per liter per gallon or 13 milligrams per liter per 5 gallons at a pH of 3.2—3.5. Again, one can also use potassium metabisulfite powders and ¼ teaspoon provides 195 milligrams per liter per gallon or 39 milligrams per liter per 5 gallons. Now if one really seeks accuracy, a good measuring scale is a wise investment since with it we can be much more precise in our total measurements. By doing a bit of chemistry stoichiometry, we find that the available amount of SO$_2$ in potassium metabisulfite ($K_2O_5S_2$) is 57.6% of its total weight. For example, lets say we would like to add 28 milligrams per liter SO$_2$ (0.028 grams per liter) at bottling to a 5 gallon carboy of wine. Here would be how we arrive at the proper conversion: 0.028 grams per liter x 3.785 liters per gallon x 5 gallons divided by .576 = .92 grams to be added to 5 gallons. This mathematical relationship can be used with any metabisulfite addition such as adding 70 milligrams per liter initially to white musts. So lets try this one! 0.070 grams per liter x 3.785 liters per gallon divided by .576 = 2.3 grams to be added to 5 gallons. This is a rather nice and easy mathematical formula which can be used for achieving whatever amount of SO_2 we wish to add to the musts.

Amounts of SO_2 Commonly Added at Different Intervals at Wine pH

- initial red musts (0 to 50 milligrams per liter)
- initial white musts (50 to 70 milligrams per liter)
- bottling (28 to 30 milligrams per liter)

A Chemical Test For SO_2 Available At Winemaking Stores

- place 0.01 normal iodine solution in buret
- pipette 10 milliliters of wine into a beaker (with reds also add 150 milliliters of distilled water)
- add 5 milliliters of dilute sulfuric acid (H_2SO_4) into beaker
- add 2—3 milliliters of 1% starch solution
- titrate the iodine into the beaker until a faint purple is reached
- record the amount of iodine used
- Calculation 3200 x volume of iodine used x 0.01(normality of the iodine) = SO_2 level in the wine

Yeast Nutrients

Since wild yeasts can grow naturally in grape musts it is obvious that most musts contain adequate amounts of nutrients for yeast to at least get a good start on fermentation. However, quite often grape musts do not contain adequate amounts of nitrogen substances and the essential B vitamins for fermentation to go to completion especially if we are using wine yeast. A lack of nitrogen in the form of ammonia will soon limit sugar utilization by the yeasts in the must and it will also soon limit protein production. This is especially true during the early exponential growth phase of the yeast when they are growing and reproducing rapidly. It is not quite as important later on in fermentation since the autolytic breakdown of dead yeast reintroduces nutrients back into the must. But, unless the yeast get a good reproductive start there may not be a long fermentation to worry about. So, it is very important that musts initially contain adequate amounts of nutrients to ensure that the yeast will grow quickly and that then there will be plenty of broken down dead ones which can provide new nutrients for the ones growing later on in the fermentation.. This can easily be accomplished by adding yeast nutrients in the form of diammonium hydrogen phosphate $(NH_4)_2HPO_4$ and certain B vitamins. In fact, Cornell University, which is a major wine education university, advises adding 1 gram per liter diammonium phosphate to ensure complete fermentation and to also reduce the chance of producing too much stinky hydrogen sulfide.

Primary Fermentation

The home winemaker has by now meticulously taken all of the steps necessary in order to start the primary fermentation. So now it is up to nature to take over and change the grape into the wine. This of course means that the yeast must become activated and start fermenting the sugars in the must. Each yeast species is different in regards to how it accomplishes this important task and many types of yeast exist to further complicate matters. The vast yeast collection at the Central Bureau Voor Schimmelcultures in the Netherlands contains greater than 4500 natural yeast types (isolates) which have been described in Mycology literature as consisting of 640 species and 75 Genera. Each type has its own growing abilities but generally speaking, most of them only grow aerobically and so seldom are found in grape musts since they really do not ferment sugars. Here is where SACCHAROMYCES CEREVISIAE strains are highly unique in that they are both aerobic and anaerobic in their growing phases. This so-called "Crabtree Effect" is also highly unusual since these yeast also have the ability to produce ethyl alcohol during both their aerobic and anaerobic phases. That is actually very strange since ethyl alcohol is not commonly made during the time of aerobic respiration. Actually, most of the ethyl alcohol production occurs during the longer, slow anaerobic growth phase with only small amounts produced during the brief aerobic phase.

The Initial Primary Fermentation

If one starts their fermentation with either fresh or frozen non-sterilized juices, a number of wild yeast will initially be activated and they will start to grow in the must aerobically. Typical species are KLOECKERA APICULATA and HANSENIASPORA UVARUM and they will immediately start to grow aerobically in the must even if wine yeast are also added at the beginning of fermentation. Normally these wild species will only grow for about 4—6 days and they often actually contribute to the complexities of the wine by producing various fruity esters, glycerol, and fusel oils. Typically, primary fermentation occurs in a vessel (open container) which allows oxygen to enter into it since it is most important that oxygen is present at the start of this activity. The importance of oxygen additions at this beginning point deals with the fact that all yeast, including SACCHAROMYCES CEREVISIAE, need oxygen immediately so that they can synthesize three important growth factors. They are ergosterol (a steroid needed for cell membrane functions), nicotinic acid (a B vitamin needed for energy production), and various unsaturated fatty acids (needed for the actual production of their cell membranes). Without this initial blast of oxygen, the yeast will never be able to grow into the large populations needed to complete the fermentation. Also this initial oxygen addition in red musts favors the early production of acetaldehyde which quickly aids in the formation of anthocyanin-tannin polymer complexes which makes the wine more colorful.

Usually the aerobic stage of primary fermentation occurs for 5—6 days and then the wine yeast change their energy making requirements and then proceed to ferment the sugars slowly under totally anaerobic conditions.

The Phases Of Yeast Growth and Fermentation (SACCHAROMYCES CEREVISIAE)

- Lag Phase—The yeast upon being added to the must become activated and try to adjust to their new environment. Those that are able to start to grow equal the amount that can not respond and die. Those that live produce ergosterol, nicotinic acid, and unsaturated fatty acids with the use of oxygen.
- Exponential or Log Phase—This is the phase of active logarithmic growth when the yeast are dividing rapidly producing a high fermentation rate in the must. It is dependent on nutrient and temperature conditions with a higher growth rate at higher temperatures.
- Stationary Phase—As fermentation continues, the decrease in available nutrients and the accumulation of toxic carboxylic acids causes reproductive yeast growth to equal yeast death rates. Fermentation continues but at a much slower rate.
- Decline Phase—The increasing lack of nutrients, including sugars, and the toxic carboxylic acids slowly cause all yeast to either die or to become highly inactive.
- Secondary (Anaerobic) Fermentation

After the vigorous carbon dioxide bubbling of primary oxygenated growth has slowed down (5—6 days), it is time to drain (rack) the must into a anaerobic vessel which is usually a 5 or 6 gallon carboy which contains an airlock. The yeast then slowly ferment the rest of the sugars into ethyl alcohol. Usually around ½ of the initial sugar in the must remains to be fermented so its end stage can be easily observed when CO_2 bubbles quit coming out of the airlock.

An Aid to Ensuring That Anaerobic Fermentation Continues

As recently shown, wine yeast due to their overall metabolic activities not only produce ethyl alcohol but also slowly produce the toxic by-products octanoic and decanoic acids. These carboxylic acids are toxic to the yeast since they literally react with and remove from the interior of the yeast cells various critical nutrients and amino acids which are necessary for yeast viability. A simple solution to this problem is to add yeast hulls (ghosts) to the fermenting must when it is transferred from the primary fermentation vessel to the anaerobic vessel. Readily available, these yeast hulls quickly absorb the toxic carboxylic acids and then settle them to the bottom of the carboy. Yeast hulls are of a further benefit in that some of them also slowly decompose liberating much needed sterols and unsaturated fatty acids which new yeast cannot synthesize since oxygen is not available in this anaerobic fermenting condition. Typical yeast hull additions call for .45—.9 grams per gallon and again are an excellent and inexpensive addition which aids in allowing fermentation to go to completion.

The Value Of A Good Racking

Back in the days of Puritanical America one tried to avoid a good racking but in the world of wine positive benefits are surely obtained by periodically racking the wine. Of course, it is known by professional enologists that allowing wine to stand on the lees for extended times may contribute to the complexities of some wines. However, the potential problems usually encountered negate most of the benefits so most amateurs are wise to keep the new wine as clear as possible. Also, periodical rackings not only help to clarify the wine but also remove toxic by-products and many of the potential spoilage substances produced from the metabolic activities of the yeast and from yeast decomposition.

Initiating The Malolactic Fermentation

When one racks a new wine, additional amounts of oxygen are introduced into the must which is not too bad for reds but may lead to the negative oxidation of white musts. So, with whites it is necessary to add back to the must an addition of SO_2 and even some red musts should receive a small amount of this gas. However, at racking if one wishes to initiate the malolactic fermentation at this time, one must be very careful in adding the SO_2 since LEUCONOSTOC OENOS can only survive at an SO_2 level of about 13 milligrams per liter. Now, as previously stated, many home winemakers like to initiate the malolactic fermentation after the 2nd racking. At this time period, most of the SO_2 is bound to other substances, ethyl alcohol concentrations which can inhibit this bacterial species are moderate, and if yeast hulls have been added then few toxic carboxylic acids are present in the must. But remember, whenever we start this process it is important to rehydrate these bacterial cultures first before adding them to the must and this is a very easy procedure.

Rehydrating Malolactic Bacterial Cultures

- Makeup a pint of dilute grape juice
- Adjust the pH to 3.6 using tartaric acid or calcium carbonate
- add a small amount of yeast nutrient extract
- add the dehydrated bacteria culture
- allow to sit and it will activate within 24 hours
- add to must

At the time of adding this culture to the must it is also wise to add more yeast nutrients since these malolactic acid bacteria require a very high amount of nutrients and most of the available nutrients in the must have already been used up. Within a reasonably short period of time, these bacteria should then convert all of the malic acid into lactic acid and they should also produce small amounts of diacetyl molecular substances which in small amounts adds a slight buttery aspect which is desirable in many wines The time it will take this fermentation to go to completion varies but home winemakers can purchase a simple chromatography test (available at winemaking outlets) which will show when all of the malic acid has been removed from the wine must. This simple test uses a small amount of wine, chromatography paper, and a solvent which separates out the different fixed acids found in the wine. A lack of malic acid showing up on the paper shows that it has been totally made into the milder tasting lactic acid. Upon completion of this activity, it is always wise to rack again and to then add 50 milligrams per liter SO_2 which will destroy any remaining lactic acid bacteria since if they are allowed to remain they may produce various off-flavors in the bottled wine.

Cold Stabilization

Although most warm weather grapes are notoriously low in acids this as previously shown is not true of cold weather grapes whether they be LABRUSCA or French hybrid varieties. Although deacidification helps, more concepts of chemistry can come into play in further reducing the high acidity encountered in these wines. Grape plants, especially grown in cold climates, take up through their roots potassium ions which they then incorporate into their fruits. During fermentation, these potassium ions slowly combine with tartaric acid molecules forming potassium bitartrate salts and free hydrogen ions. This slow chemical reaction is ideal since the addition of the hydrogen ions to the must slightly reduces the pH which is great. Potassium bitartrate, commonly known as cream of tartar, binds with colloids, and tannin complexes in the must and these complexes are highly water soluble.

So, from a chemical standpoint, if one could then precipitate out the potassium bitartrate complexes, then one could further reduce the acidity of the wine and yet still maintain a low pH due to the production of the extra hydrogen ions. This precipitation can be accomplished through the technique known as Cold Stabilization which reduces the solubility of potassium bitartrate.

The Technique of Cold Stabilization

An important chemistry note to remember is that the solubility of potassium bitartrate decreases as the alcohol concentration increases in the wine must. To make things even better, chilling the must further decreases the solubility of this salt and this is what Cold Stabilization is all about! The idea is to ferment the must to dryness where the alcohol level is at its maximum value, and then place the fermentation vessel in a cold area slightly below freezing. Actually the entire process can be accomplished in 5 days at—5.5°C (22°F) or in two weeks at—3.9°C (25°F). This is rather easily done since most winemakers who use cold weather grapes also live in cold weather climates and a nice garage often works quite handily. Timing of course is pretty important but a little bit of winter weather timing quite easily accomplishes the task! If one is afraid that relatively low temperatures may freeze their wine, then slightly below freezing temperatures will work but it will take a bit longer. If the weather is warm, an old refrigerator has also been known to do the trick! What ultimately will soon happen in this cold environment is that the potassium bitartrate crystals will soon form insoluble crystals which will sink to the bottom of the vessel where they can be racked out while the wine is still cold. So, Cold Stabilization is a rather nice chemical concept which easily reduces the acidity of these often tart wines.

COLD STABILIZATION

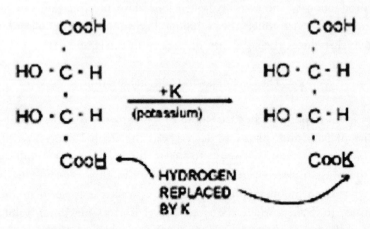

A Test To See If All Of The Potassium Bitartrate Is Gone

- Take a small sample of wine
- Adjust the pH to 3.6 by either adding dilute hydrochloric acid (lowers it) or dilute sodium hydroxide (raises it)
- Chill the wine sample and if crystals appear at this pH then all of the potassium bitartrate has not been removed—Cold Stabilize for a longer period of time!

CHAPTER 4

Achieving Perfect Balance

"We could in the United States make as great a variety of wines as are in Europe, not exactly of the same kinds, but doubtless as good." Thomas Jefferson

The time has finally arrived where the fermentation is over and the wine looks pretty darn good. It sure would be nice if all we had to do was bottle the wine and give it a bit of time to mature. But, a wine chemist would say that a final analysis is necessary to ensure that the product will as good can be expected. So, it is highly reasonable to assume that just about every wine made by the home winemaker can be enhanced by making some final adjustments. So, let us take a brief look and examine these final procedures so that we can make that close to perfect wine on a yearly basis.

Balance

According to Food Science 430 at Cornell University, "Balance in wine refers to the interaction and harmony between two or more of the wine's constituents". For example, sugar and acid levels often are balanced together and the wine should not be neither too sweet or too acidic. If too much acid dominates the sugar, we will be left with a harsh, sharp, and acidic wine. If it contains too much sugar it will taste too rich, sugary, soft, and limp. If both too much sugar and acids are in the wine then what we will have is a sweet-tart character which is also undesirable.

Tannins and acids are two other ingredients in wine that must come into proper balance for a tasty product. This concept is readily explained by the French enologist Emile Peyand in his book "The Taste Of Wine". He rather nicely describes the harmony between tannins and acids with the following ideas in mind.

• The less tannic a wine is, the more acidity it can support.
• The higher a red wine is in tannins, the lower should be the acidity.
• The combination of high acid and high tannins make the hardest and most astringent wines.
• A wine tolerates acidity better when its alcohol content is higher.
• A considerable amount of tannin is more acceptable if acidity is low and alcohol is high.

Achieving The Proper Balance of a Dry Wine Every Time

• Use good wine chemistry to ensure that the initial wine must contains proper amounts of sugars, acids, and tannins.
• Ferment to Dryness
• Adjust the now dry wine by adding to it small amounts of sugar which will balance the acidity of the dry wine without making it sweet

Chemical Adjustments

Conducting a simple chemical analysis of one's finished wine is just the same as going back over a math test you have just taken in a math course. It just makes common sense to review one's work since mistakes can be caught and fixed! For example, most finished wines should have a final fixed acid concentration between 0.6— 0.8% with reds being more towards the bottom and whites more towards the top. If proper techniques were observed during fermentation, then the acid level should not have changed. But, if the must was not adjusted properly before fermentation, then it is not too late at this time to adjust it to proper levels. Addition of tartaric acid can raise the acidity of a low acid wine and also at the same time lower the pH by freeing hydrogen ions into the wine. Any wine below a pH of 3.1 may be too sour and a wine with a pH greater than 3.7 may only offer a flat, pop-like taste. Also as previously shown, one can raise the pH of a high acid wine through amelioration or potassium carbonate additions. If the wine is too dry, sugar can be added through techniques soon to be addressed. Finally, if tannins are too low then one can add to the wine additional tannins in the form of grape powder tannins.

Sugar Additions or Sweet vs Dry

Even when a wine is fermented to dryness, it will still contain some residual sugar mostly in the form of arabinose, rhamnose, and xylose molecules which are essentially tasteless. These unusual sugars are only found in small concentrations in grapes, and yeast do not have the ability to ferment them so they just stay in the wine. Many certainly enjoy a dry wine but in order to achieve that perfect harmony and balance it is a good idea to add back to the wine small amounts of sugar which if done correctly can still keep the wine dry tasting. However, people are selective and many actually enjoy wines with higher amounts of sugar in it. So, if you like wines with differing sweetness levels, then you as the home winemaker can adjust your products using the concept of Brix. For example, we know that 1.6 ounces of table sugar added to a gallon of wine will raise the residual sugar level by ½% Brix. Most home winemakers not using scales, go with the concept that 2 ounces (4 tablespoons) will raise it by ½% which is actually pretty close to 1.6 ounces.

One Lump or Two In My Wine

sugar/gal	tablespoons	to achieve Brix	residual sugar
up to 4 oz	up to 8	up to 1%	dry
4—8 oz	8—16	1—2%	semi-dry
8—12 oz	16—24	2—3%	semi-sweet
over 12	24+	over 3%	sweet

In the world of measurements, 16 tablespoons = 1 cup so a nice general rule is that we can raise 5 gallons of wine 1 Brix by adding to it just a tad more than one cup of sugar which isn't perfect but pretty close.

Another useful way of determining how sweet we desire our wines to be is to mess around once again with the hydrometer and take specific gravity readings. For example, a dry wine should have a hydrometer reading slightly less than 1.000. A semi-sweet wine should read between 1.001 to 1.005 and a sweet wine from 1.010 to as high as 1.020. Now these levels are just generalities but all one has to really do is add back to the wine sugar until these hydrometer reading are reached. So, with a little bit of practice, the home winemaker will develop their own perfected hydrometer readings which give them their personal sweetness levels for whatever wines they make.

Potassium Sorbate

It would actually be a monumental mistake to add sugar to wines and then immediately bottle the stuff. Lurking in these finished wines are many wine yeasts that have been resting ever since the fermentation ceased. This influx of new sugar molecules is just what they need and they will soon restart the fermentation process, producing carbon dioxide gas which will ultimately blow out the cork creating one big mess. At the worst extreme, a very tight cork can actually cause the bottle to explode into flying glass fragments! Luckily, once again chemistry comes to the rescue for the home winemaker! Sorbic acid is a short chained fatty acid widely used in the food industry to control the growth of fungi and is harmless to humans. When added to wine, it rapidly enters dormant yeast cells where it inactivates dehydrogenase enzymes which normally allow the yeast to utilize carbon substances. So what essentially happens is that the sorbic acid stops the yeast from being able to grow and reproduce by budding. Since sorbic acid by itself is not water soluble, it is sold in winemaking stores as potassium sorbate which is quite water soluble and easy to use.

SORBIC ACID AN EXCELLENT STABILIZER USED IN SWEETENED WINES

$$H-\underset{\underset{H}{|}}{\overset{\overset{H}{|}}{C}}-\overset{\overset{H}{|}}{C}=\overset{\overset{H}{|}}{C}-\overset{\overset{H}{|}}{C}=\overset{\overset{H}{|}}{C}-\overset{\overset{O}{\|}}{C}-OH$$

An interesting point in regards to the finished wine is that sorbic acid works synergistic with SO_2 and additions of this gas not only aides in killing unwanted microbes, but the SO_2 also forms a complex with the sorbic acid keeping it from being oxidized by oxygen at the time of bottling. Although the BATF allows additions of 300 milligrams per liter, its taste detection is around 150 milligrams per liter and so the higher limit is usually too much for us to add and not at all necessary. Typically 80 milligrams per liter of sorbate and 30 milligrams per liter SO_2 (roughly ¼ tsp/5 gal) is plenty to inhibit the dormant yeast. However, most home winemakers would rather be on the safe side since they are not interested in wines that blow their corks or even explosions! As a result it is very safe and reasonable to add 200—250 milligrams per liter potassium sorbate which equals about 1 gram per gallon. This equals about ½ teaspoon per gallon or 2 ½ teaspoons for 5 gallons. In fact, many home winemakers believe that 1 tablespoon for 5 gallons is the magical amount to use. The usual procedure to follow is to first filter the wine to remove as many dormant yeast as possible, add sorbate, add SO_2, and then add back the desired amount of sugar a few days later. A quick word of caution though is that long term aging of these sweetened wines is not advised since the sorbate will slowly react with ethyl alcohol forming ethyl sorbate which has a pineapple-celery odor. To make matters worse, if any lactic acid bacteria are still present in the wine they can react with the sorbate forming 2,4-hexadien-1-ol which produces "Geranium Tone" which is not good and will be further discussed in Chapter 5.

Glycerol Additions

As already noted, glycerol is a normal by-product of yeast metabolism and so is found in wines in small concentrations. Many enologists feel that by adding a small amount of glycerol to wines at the end of fermentation will make them more full-bodied. This addition may also aid in making high acid wines somewhat less astringent and also at the same time more full-bodied. Typical additions are in the range of 1—5 milliliters per liter of wine. Be sure to add the glycerol after fermentation is over since if Lactic Acid bacteria are present, then they can convert glycerol ($C_3H_8O_3$) into a undesirable substance known as acrolein (CH_2CHCHO) which has a very bitter taste.

Fining

Occasionally a finished wine will suffer from problems related to the fact that excess proteins, which should have been removed during racking, actually remain in solution in the wine forming a haze. Other problems often encountered at this time deal with having excessive tannins in the wine which cause it to be way too astringent and bitter. Finally, one may just encounter some hard to define tastes that makes this very early wine just taste horrible. Once again chemistry comes to the rescue where certain chemical substances can be added to these early wines which will cause these problems to be overcome. We call this process "Fining" and when done correctly really can help change a bad situation into a pleasant surprise.

Protein Stabilization

Proteins, being positively charged, readily stay dissolved in the polar water molecules of wine. As a result they may form a protein haze which reduces the clarity of wine due to their light dispersing properties. This is seldom a problem in red wines since the proteins naturally bind to the phenol-tannin complexes as already shown. These large complexes then sink to the bottom where they are removed with periodical rackings. However, whites are naturally low in phenol-tannin complexes and so protein haze is often a problem in white wines. The main fining material used for removing proteins from white wines is American bentonite $(Al_2O_3:4SiO_2-H_2O)$. Also known as "Wyoming Clay", it is a complex of hydrated aluminum silicate. Most types available are actually a form of sodium bentonite which have the best protein binding ability so is the best type to use. When placed into the wine, it quickly swells and offers many negatively charged areas for binding to the positively charged proteins causing this nasty haze. The protein-bentonite complexes then slowly settle to the bottom ultimately removing the haze. Usually 1—2 grams per gallon is sufficient but unfortunately a major disadvantage of using bentonite is that it produces very large fluffy lees and a fair amount of wine is lost at racking. So, a rather neat tip is to add the bentonite during Cold Stabilization since the potassium bitartrate crystals will compact the lees and less wine will be lost upon racking.

Excessive Tannins

Too many bitter tasting tannins are certainly not good since the wine just will not taste right. At bottling they can also react with oxygen forming long polymers of brown pigments which defract light causing hazes known as "Oxidative Casse". Furthermore, chilling wine may cause a protein-tannin haze to occur so excessive tannins can lead up to many problems. So, we should fine wine containing excessive tannins and a number of common fining agents can be used which are basically protein substances which will bind to the tannins and ultimately sink them to the bottom.

Gelatin (Unflavored)

- made from animal connective tissue and contains protein amino acids
- binds to tannins, removes dead yeast, and other off-flavors
- 2 grams per 5 gallons (1 teaspoon) added to warm water and then added to red wines will bind to tannins and soon settle them to the bottom
- 1/16 to ¼ grams (5 gallons) added to warm water and then added to white wines will bind to tannins
- Gelatin Haze—Sometimes a gelatin induced haze may develop after fining with this ingredient so here is a helpful tip. A few days before the gelatin addition, add a small amount of Kieselol which is a suspension of silicon dioxide which will precipitate the excess gelatin to the bottom after it has done its job of removing excess tannins.

Isinglass

- made from the air bladders of sturgeon fish and is high in protein
- luckily this stuff is ground up and sterilized

- is excellent for removing excess tannins from wines
  0.01 grams to 0.07 grams per gallon are added to the wine
- in the liquid form use 1 milliliter per gallon

Casein

- the major protein in milk
- for years many winemakers have actually used skim milk to
  remove tannins and also to remove oxidized colors
- purchase it as potassium cassinate and add at the rate of 0.1 to
  1 gram per gallon
- care must be taken not to add too much or wine will taste and
  smell cheesy

Albumin

- many use actual egg-whites which contain this protein (1/2 of
  an egg white whipped with a pinch of salt added to 5
  gallons)
- powdered egg whites are easier to use (2.5—4 grams for 5
  gallons)
- removes tannins, lessens astringency, and adds brilliance to
  reds
- removes excess oak flavors if to much oak has been added

Sparkolloid

- it is a form of calcinated diatomaceous earth
- excellent for removing tannins
- forms very compact lees so not much wine is lost
- seldom strips the wine of any sensory substances
- often added after bentonite treatment to compact the lees
- use 0.5 to 1.5 grams per gallon
- be patient since it settles slowly

Oak Chip Additions

Everybody knows that wine and oak barrels go hand in hand and that wine barrels have been used for many years to not only age wine but to also add more complexity to the wine. Although some home winemakers make use of them they can make things pretty complicated and require lots of upkeep. So, what many home winemakers do instead of using barrels is to add oak chips or liquid oak to their wines and allow these substances to slowly add the oak sensory and bouquet aspects in this manner. They can readily be added either during active fermentation or at the end when the wine is resting. These easy to use substances are full of oak lignins which contain coniferyl and sinapyl alcohols which slowly leech out into the wine. In the acidic condition of wine, these phenolic nonflavonoids form sinapaldehyde, coniferaldehyde, and vanillin compounds which tend to give woody, smokey, and vanilla flavors to the wine.

**WHAT THE ACID CONDITIONS OF WINE
DO TO OAK SUBSTANCES (AN EXAMPLE)**

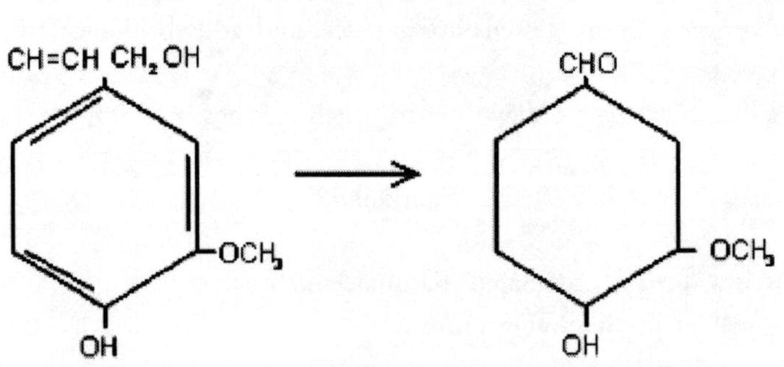

CONIFERYL
ALCOHOL

VANILLIN

Oak chips are often added during the initial fermentation since carbon dioxide bubbles move the chips around allowing greater extraction in a lesser time and the chips will soon settle out to be racked off. However, an excellent alternative to chips and which is often added after fermentation has ceased is Oak-Mor. It is finely granular, does not impart a "greenish" character to the wine, works in a couple of days, and settles very easily. Typical additions call for 3.8—19 grams per gallon of Oak-Mor and imparts a very fine oak flavor to the wines which are known to benefit from this procedure.

The Benefits of a Final Filtering

- produces a brilliantly clear wine
- eliminates various particles which racking may miss
- larger filters pad sizes remove very few colors and aromas
- pad filters less than 0.5 microns remove any remaining bacteria
- using a pad filter of 0.65—1 microns removes left over yeast

Aging

Patience is a virtue and of course wine must be aged, but only the premium, hardy wines truly benefit from long term aging. These include such red varietals as Cabernet Sauvignon, Pinot noir, and Syrah and white varietals such as Riesling, Chardonnay, and Sauvignon blanc. These well known varietals may lose some of their fruity qualities with long aging, but will develop much better overall sensory qualities. On the other hand, most wines made by home winemakers are much better if consumed rather early when they still are full of pleasing fruity esters and have a much fresher taste.

The Chemistry of Aging

- At bottling some oxygen gets in the wine and reacts with ethyl alcohol forming acetaldehyde. In red wines, the acetaldehyde then causes a faster polymerization between red anthocyanins and flavonoid tannins making the colors more stable.
- The addition of oxygen at bottling slowly decreases the bitterness of tannins.
- Some of the oxygen addition combines with higher alcohols forming ethanol esters and other alcohols which increases fruitiness in a short time.
- Ethyl alcohol has time to react with acetaldehyde forming acetals (hydroxy-2-propanone) which has a slight jasmine smell and a nutty-aftertaste.
- Carbon dioxide is saturated in the wine at bottling but with aging it is slowly removed reducing the sense of too much acidity in the wine.
- With too much aging, acetic acid esters, isoamyl esters, and isobutyl esters hydrolyze back to their corresponding acids and alcohols and the wine then tastes less fruity.
- The floral monoterpenes are slowly converted to monoterpene oxides which tend to be odorless due to their high aroma threshold.
- Acid levels tend to remain unchanged during the aging process.

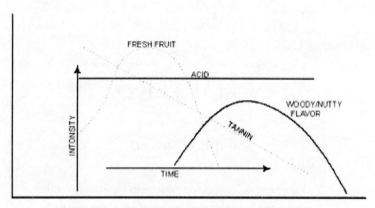

FRESH FRUIT

ACID

WOODY/NUTTY
FLAVOR

INTENSITY

TANNIN

TIME

HOW WINES CHANGE WITH AGE

CHAPTER 5

Wine Disorders

"In Europe we thought of wine as something as healthy and normal as food and also a great giver of happiness and well being and delight. Drinking wine was not a snobbism nor a sign of sophistication nor a cult; It was as natural as eating and to me as necessary." Ernest Hemingway

The wines finally been bottled, aged, and ready for consumption. We eagerly open the bottle expecting all sorts of pleasant surprises. We anticipate a wonderful aroma and a pleasing, balanced taste. Instead we are met with some nasty smells and tastes which are obvious even to the non-wine tasting expert. What went wrong since directions were followed, sanitation was observed, and everything went according to plan? Well, unfortunately it often does not take much for something to go astray in the world of home winemaking. A simple example of this is a common problem that can occur while aging the wines in carboys and not catching the fact that oxygen is slowly seeping into the wine. This simply can occur if the water evaporates out of the airlock and the problem is not caught in time. Even pressure changes occurring in the wine can force the rubber stopper from being air tight on the airlock. If either of these situations occur, oxidative film forming yeast may start growing in the wine producing off-flavors, off-smells, and soon lower alcohol concentrations which further lowers the stability of the wine. These wild, film forming yeast are able to grow off of ethyl alcohol and wine acids producing noxious levels of acetaldehyde (bruised apples), acetic acid (vinegary), and ethyl acetate (acetone) molecules. Many of them are resistant to SO_2 additions and so once they start growing, they are really hard to stop. Luckily, if observed early, one can filter using a 0.5—1 micron filter pad, boost the alcohol level in the wine (add alcohol), and maintain low storage temperatures. This can be a common problem so always periodically check your airlocks and unfortunately this is only one problem often encountered by the home winemaker.

It would certainly be useful if there existed some basic visual, odoriferous, or tasting concepts which the home winemaker could readily associate with problems they encounter with their final product. It would also be nice if some of the problems could be rectified before the wine is totally ruined. Fortunately, most of the problems encountered can be readily separated into categories and solutions do exist for most of them as we shall soon see!

Problems During Fermentation

It is wise to start with visual appearance since a cloudy wine tends to turn off most people and this is one of the reasons commercially produced wines are almost always filtered. Of course, true wine connoisseurs know that a well aged, premium red wine will naturally deposit some sediment over time which is quite normal and acceptable. But most home made wines are not aged for long periods of time and they should be as clear as possible. So let us examine some of the possible sources of cloudiness and offer some positive solutions to the problem.

I.   Pectic Haze—Although most warm weather grapes are naturally low in pectins this is not the case for fruit wines and even cold weather grapes. Pectins have already been discussed and they usually cause serious cloudiness if not broken into small substances.

Solution

A. Add pectic enzymes to the must at the beginning of fermentation.B.   A simple chemical test is available which will tell if cloudiness is due to pectins. Take 25 milliliters of wine and add it to 50 milliliters acidulated 95% ethyl alcohol (contains 1% hydrochloric acid). The formation of a gel in a few minutes shows that the pectins are still present in the wine. Regular old isopropyl alcohol (rubbing alcohol) will also work.

C. If pectins are still present prior to bottling, double the amount of pectin enzymes and add to the resting wine. Allow time for the pectin fragments to settle and then rack off the must.

II. Protein Haze—Charged proteins in wine tend to clump together and they are also attracted to polar water molecules in the wine. This delays protein settling forming a protein haze in the wine. As previously noted, this problem usually occurs in white wines which naturally have less tannins available to form tannin-protein complexes which normally sink to the bottom of the fermenting musts. Reds naturally contain many tannins so seldom suffer from a protein haze and so usually are not much of a problem.

Solution

A. It is usually not advised to add tannins to white fermenting musts to achieve protein settling since the excess tannins may make the wine too astringent.

B. Adding bentonite, especially during cold stabilization, is an excellent way to remove proteins from the wine.

III. Film Forming Oxidative Yeast—As already noted these nasty native yeast will readily grow in wines if oxygen is allowed to seep into the storage vessels. They will soon produce a distinct chalky film which is observed mostly at the top of the vessel and can easily ruin a wine.

Solution

A. Always observe and practice good sanitation.
B. Make sure all aging vessels, carboys, bottles, etc are topped up leaving little head space for oxygen.
C. Make sure rubber stoppers are always on tight and that airlocks contain water.
D. Add a small amount of metabisulfite to the water in the airlock to inhibit microbe growth.
E. If the problem has already occurred, finely filter to remove the yeast, add alcohol, SO_2, and then bottle.

Color Is Not Good

Occasionally one may experience a finished wine which just seems to have an unsightly color or even that the color is too light.

Solution

A. If using fresh grapes make sure that they have been pressed well to allow the pigments to be readily extracted.
B. Limit SO_2 additions to initial red musts so that color extraction of pigments is enhanced.
C. Too much fining may remove colors from wines.
D. Too much fine filtering may remove colored pigments from wines.
E. Limit oxygen additions at bottling so that only small amounts of acetaldehyde is formed. Too much acetaldehyde produces besides awful tastes, bad dark colors

F. If a white wine has a nasty dark color, one can take dried egg shells (bake in an oven) and add them to the wine. They will absorb the off-colors and ultimately precipitate where they can then be racked off. This process does not affect the taste of the wine.

G. The use of metallic fermentation vessels may sometimes add metals to the wine causing dark purple or brown hazes to develop. One may add ½ teaspoon of citric acid per gallon or ½ ounce of citric acid to 5 gallons to correct this problem.

H. If a wine is very weak in coloration, concentrated pigments can be purchased which will add colors to the wine.

Odor is Fine But The Taste Is Bad

Although most off-tastes are usually accompanied by bad odors, this is not always the case. Many factors influence the tastes of wine but some are more common than others and seem to quite often happen to homemade wines.

I. The Wine Has Little Fruitiness—Most wines whether they be sweet or dry should still have a bit of fruitiness. Sometimes though the fruity character is not very pronounced even after a short aging period.

Solution

A. The next time use specific wine yeasts such as Cotes Des Blanc or Steinberg which are known for producing many fruity esters.

B. A low fermentation temperature favors the production of more fruity esters such as isoamyl, isobutyl, and hexyl acetates.

C. The long term aging of fruity tasting wines is usually not recommended because fruity esters naturally tend to revert back to their parent organic acids and alcohols. So, the solution is to consume fruity wines after only a short aging period.

D. Although most monoterpene alcohols are usually thought of as adding to flowery sensations in wine, they can also contribute to fruitiness. However, with long aging, especially if oxygen is present, they will change into monoterpene oxides which are not fruity. Once again limit the amount of oxygen.

II. Wine Has a Sweet-Sour Taste—Most consumers would not be amused with a sweet-sour taste in their wine and to make matters worse, it is often accompanied by a lingering hot sensation. This condition is usually associated with a situation known as Mannitic Fermentation or what is also called Lactic Sours. As previously noted, lactic acid bacteria are often added to wines to convert malic acid into lactic acid through the malolactic fermentation. However, in high pH musts, these bacteria can start to ferment both glucose and fructose. This happens especially during early fermentation when lots of these sugars are available. In this Mannitic Fermentation the glucose is converted into acetic acid (vinegary) and lactic acid molecules. The fructose is converted into a rather unpleasant tasting sugar known as mannitol $(C_6H_8(OH)_6$. These chemicals make up the sweet-sour tastes and this problem may go undetected until the bottle is opened since little acetone smelling ethyl acetate molecules are generated by these bacteria and so the wine might actually smell fine at the time of bottling.

Solution

A. Initially add SO_2 to musts to destroy any wild lactic acid bacteria.

B. Maintain a low pH in the wine by adding tartaric acid or phosphoric acid if the pH is too high.

C. Maintain an adequate amount of molecular SO_2 throughout the entire winemaking process.

D. If malolactic fermentation is desired, add them to the must towards the end of fermentation. At this time sugar concentrations are quite low.

E. Make sure that enough SO_2 is added at bottling to ensure the destruction of all lactic acid bacteria since they can grow in bottled wine.

III Astringency and Bitterness

Astringency in wine is usually due to an excessive amounts of tannins in the wine. Bitterness is mainly due to the phenolic fractions along with a high alcohol content since we know that ethyl alcohol can enhance both bitterness intensity and duration!

Solution

A. Make sure to limit the amounts of stems and seeds in the must during the primary fermentation.

B. Rack within 5-6 days after starting the anaerobic fermentation which will help to clear many of the astringent and bitter components found in the initial must.

C. Keep the ethyl alcohol content between 10 and 12%.

D. As shown in chapter 4, fining with gelatin is a great way of removing the astringent tannins from wines.

IV Soda Pop Taste

On occasion a new wine may just taste flat like soda pop which has been left exposed to the air too long. This is usually a problem which occurs when the home enologist has just let the must ferment without using any of their knowledge of chemistry.

Solution

A. Study the chemistry of grapes to wine!

B. Adjust the fixed acid levels so that the correct amount of tartaric acid is in the wine.

C. A flat wine is usually low in tannins so add 1/8 teaspoon per gallon of grape tannin and wait 12 hours. Then taste the wine and if it is still too flat add 1/8 teaspoon more. Continue this process until you are satisfied with the taste.

D. If the pH of this wine is too high add phosphoric acid to the wine to reduce the pH to typical wine pH levels.

Odor and Taste Are Both Bad

Usually when something has gone wrong in the winemaking process one experiences both a nasty smell and also a bad taste. These two sensory perceptions usually go hand in hand due to chemical reactions which have occurred and the problem may or may not be curable. Of course, it is reasonable to assume that everybody at one time or another has smelled or tasted foods which have been spoiled by some sort of microbial contamination. Such may even be the case for the home winemaker in that the smells and odors are obnoxious. Luckily, due to the low pH of wine, relatively few microbes such as molds and bacteria can grow and destroy your hard work. Fortunately, this is also true of the bacteria that cause food poisoning in humans since they can't grow in the low pH of wine. Yet, a few bacterial strains, and of course wild yeast, do contaminate wines on occasions and they can readily ruin a sound wine. Other off-tastes and smells are not microbial in nature but instead are due to some strange chemical reactions occurring in the wine. Fortunately, it is possible to summarize by far the most common problems, both microbial and chemical, and in some cases even offer various remedies so that not all is not lost and that we can learn not to repeat the same mistake.

Oh No Its Vinegar !

In days of old, many individuals would naturally ferment apple juice and let it sit exposed to oxygen. Ultimately, vinegar was produced which was a great preservative in the days of no refrigerators. Vinegar is usually 95% water and 5% acetic acid molecules and the process of making it is due to both yeast and bacteria working on the juice.

THE MAKING OF VINEGAR

$$\underset{\text{ETHYL ALCOHOL}}{\overset{\displaystyle H-\underset{\displaystyle H}{\overset{\displaystyle H}{C}}-\underset{\displaystyle H}{\overset{\displaystyle OH}{C}}-H}{}} \xrightarrow{\text{OXYGEN}} \underset{\text{ACETALDEHYDE}}{\overset{\displaystyle H-\underset{\displaystyle H}{\overset{\displaystyle H}{C}}-\overset{\displaystyle O}{C}-H}{}} \xrightarrow{H_2O} \underset{\text{ACETIC ACID}}{\overset{\displaystyle H-\underset{\displaystyle H}{\overset{\displaystyle H}{C}}-\overset{\displaystyle OH}{C}=O}{}}$$

As previously noted, all yeast during normal fermentation produce small levels of acetic acid which can positively influence the taste of wines after it reacts to form fruity acetate esters. But unfortunately it does not take much acetic acid to render a wine unfit to drink and oxygen is the chemical culprit in its overproduction. Of course, it is true in some instances certain spoilage yeast such as BRETTANOMYCES and DEKKARA will grow in oxygenated musts low in nitrogen and even in stuck fermentations. They are often a big problem in barrel fermentations since oxygen quite often slowly leaks into barrels. Even worse than these wild yeast are native airborn bacteria which naturally are found on grapes. They are known as acetic acid bacteria and early crushed grapes may contain 100 cells per milliliter and late harvest grapes may contain 10,000 to 1,000,000 cells per milliliter! They can readily grow at a low pH and even relatively high SO_2 concentrations of up to 50 milligrams per liter. They consist mainly of GLUCONOBACTER OXYDANS and smaller numbers of ACETOBACTER ACETI and they can easily convert glucose into many different products. They can also convert ethyl alcohol into acetic acid under aerobic conditions. In fact, these bacteria can cause problems during any stage of the winemaking process but usually the problem occurs either early or even after bottling if the corks are not properly sealed. During early fermentation, they can also rapidly grow if yeast growth is slow, and especially if a stuck fermentation occurs. If either of these situation happens, these bacteria will breakdown the glucose into such products as gluconic acid, lactic acid, succinic acid, and various ketones which is not at all desirable. This problem especially may occur with warm weather grapes which are low in acid and have a high pH. These bacteria do not breakdown fructose (which is very sweet tasting) and if they continue to grow during fermentation, they will also produce acetic acid leaving the wine with a sweet-sour taste. They are highly able to produce substantial amounts of acetic acid from the ethyl alcohol which is being formed during fermentation further complicating the problem.

Solution

A. This is plain and simple an oxygen induced problem so it is essential to limit the slow leakage of oxygen into fermenting vessels and bottles.

B. Maintain an adequate amount of free SO_2 throughout the entire wine making process.

C. Make sure nitrogen supplies are adequate to avoid a stuck fermentation.

D. Maintain a low pH and a good acid level.

II. The Wine Smells and Tastes Overly Nutty and Even Like Bruised Apples

Most wine enthusiasts have at some time opened a bottle of wine and have been met with these overbearing smells and tastes and usually the color of the wine is way too dark. The problem is due to the overproduction of unusually high levels of acetaldehyde and once again oxygen is the major culprit. The oxygen allows the chemical oxidation of ethyl alcohol into these high levels of acetaldehyde. As already noted, acetaldehyde is normally produced in small amounts during fermentation and it actually aids in tannin-pigment stability. It really only becomes a problem if oxygen is allowed to enter the vessels during early aging or after the wine has been bottled. It is a chemical reaction but if spoilage yeast are in the vessel then they also have the ability to further breakdown ethyl alcohol into even more acetaldehyde molecules. To make matters even worse, these spoilage yeast will also generate substantial amounts of acetic acid and ethyl acetate further ruining the wine.

Solution
A. Once again limit the amount of oxygen throughout the entire winemaking process.
B. If chalk forming spoilage film yeast are noted, fine filter, add alcohol and SO_2.
C. Maintain a small head space and make sure water is always in the airlocks.
D. Use good corks and maintain cool storage conditions.

III. The Wine Has a Pineapple-Celery or a Crushed Geranium Leaf Odor and the Taste is Bad

As shown in chapter 4, sugar additions to dry wines require the careful additions of potassium sorbate which will only impart a funny taste if this chemical is stale and old or if it is added in very high concentrations. But, even with proper additions these wines should be consumed early since long term aging may cause them to develop a taste and odor resembling a blend of pineapple-celery which is certainly not a desirable trait. The chemical reaction involved in this odor does not involve microbes but instead is due to a slow reaction occurring between the added potassium sorbate and ethyl alcohol forming a compound called ethyl sorbate.

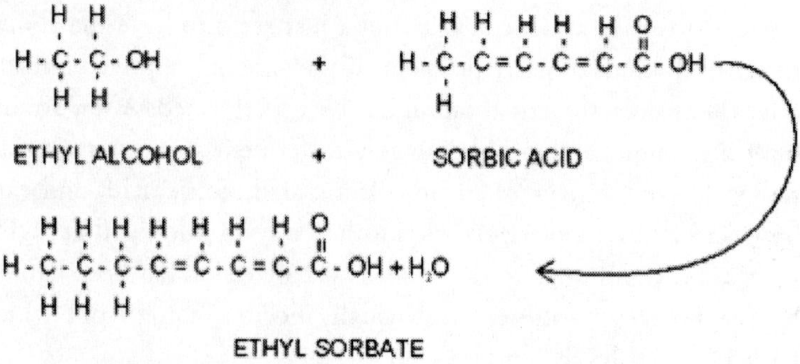

ETHYL ALCOHOL   +   SORBIC ACID

ETHYL SORBATE

The reaction shown above is rather slow but often occurs within a year of aging.

Another potential problem dealing with potassium sorbate may occur if any lactic acid bacteria are left remaining in the newly sweetened wine. Most lactic acid bacteria can convert sorbic acid (from potassium sorbate) into sorbyl alcohol which then rearranges itself in the acid conditions of wine into another alcohol, 2,4-hexadien-1-ol. This big named alcohol then reacts with ethyl alcohol in the wine to form an ether known as 2-ethoxyhexa-3,5-diene. This ether smells like crushed geranium leaves hence the term for this condition is called Geranium Tone. This chemical is actually so powerful that our olfactory nerves can smell it in parts per trillion and most people are offended by its overbearing smell and taste.

Solution

A. Maintain a low pH and adequate SO_2 and not as much potassium sorbate needs to be added to wines which have been sweetened.

B. Make sure enough SO_2 has been added to destroy all lactic acid bacteria.

C. Fine filter to remove any remaining lactic acid bacteria.

D. Consume these sweetened wines after only a short aging period of a few months to a year.

IV. Tourne

Unfortunately, lactic acid bacteria just seem to have the ability to cause all kinds of nasty problems if they are not removed quickly after the malolactic fermentation has been performed. A few strains have the unique ability of being able to ferment stable tartaric acid molecules and convert them into lactic acid, acetic acid, and carbon dioxide. This of course is another way of adding that awful vinegar taste and smell to the wine. This conversion has been named by the French, "Tourne", and usually occurs in high pH wines with low SO_2 levels.

TOURNE - COMPLICATED BUT UNDERSTANDABLE

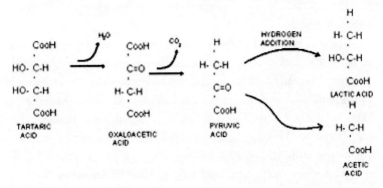

Solution

A. Maintain enough SO_2 to destroy lactic acid bacteria.

B. Maintain a low pH.

C. Filter the finished wine to remove any remaining lactic acid bacteria.

V. Mousiness

Every year millions of dollars are lost by the wine industry due to mousiness. This problem is actually just a general term that describes wines as being overly spicy, medicinal, or even having a rodent-cage litter smell. Mousiness is usually due to contamination in the wineries, especially the equipment, from a nasty spoilage yeast known as BRETTANOMYCES which is commonly called Brett.

Since this yeast is not commonly found on grapes then why should the home winemaker even worry about it? Well, since many of us purchase our juices from actual wineries, it is logical to assume that if the winery has a problem with it, then you may have received infected juice. To further compound the problem, common fruit flies, found at all wineries, pick up these yeast on their tarsi (legs) and can drop them off in your must if you live close to that establishment. Now one may say that is pretty far fetched, but actually fruit flies can be a real problem to the home winemaker during the summer when plenty of fruits are available for fermentation and wild Brett yeast may be on them. Another potential problem is that these yeast can actually live and grow off of the cellobiose in wine barrels which they convert into glucose molecules. They can also convert glucose into acetic acid, degrade ethyl alcohol, and also degrade fruity esters so they are downright disagreeable creatures which we should strive to avoid!

AN EXAMPLE OF "MOUSINESS"

COUMARIC ACID

4 - ETHYL PHENOL

OVERLY SPICY OR MEDICINAL

Solution

A. Discuss with the wineries their knowledge of Brett and as to whether they have ever experienced this problem.

B. Maintain a sanitary primary fermentation with cloth over the fermentation vessel to keep out fruit flies in the summer.

C. 0.5 Mg/L Molecular SO_2 destroys this yeast so maintain adequate levels.

D. A low pH and low fermentation temperature slows their growth.

E. Fine filtering will remove them and this should be performed as soon as possible.

VI. Rotten Egg Odors

The benefits of SO_2 additions are by now readily apparent and it is usually very difficult to make a sound wine without it. No other substance has been able to take its place as an antioxidant and microbe inhibitor. If added in proper minimal concentrations, it adds to wine complexity and allows for the selective growth of specific wine yeast. Unfortunately, if added in too high concentrations it can also contribute to some nasty sulfur smells such as the well known rotten egg smell of hydrogen sulfide (H_2S). The problem often starts in the vineyard itself since most grape growers periodically spray elemental sulfur on their grapes and vines to control the growth of many molds. Some of this residual sulfur may still be on the grapes at crush and it can be reduced into hydrogen sulfide upon coming in contact with yeast cells. Fortunately, as early fermentation proceeds, most of this hydrogen sulfide is oxidized back to elemental sulfur which precipitates to the bottom and is then racked away. Actually it should be realized that small amounts of sulfur is actually needed by yeast cells for the production of proteins, certain B vitamins, and even coenzymes which are mineral containing substances that help enzymes to function. So, normally the yeast take in through their cellular membranes various sulfur compounds, chemically rearrange them, and then normally release some of the excess produced including hydrogen sulfide. As strange as it may seem small amounts of hydrogen sulfide is a normal condition in fermenting musts. The amount liberated is partially dependent upon yeast genetics since such strains as Montrachet and Steinberg may at times liberate significant amounts of hydrogen sulfide which can occasionally become a problem. This is especially true if ammonia nitrogen and certain B vitamins are deficient in the must. It is also known that many native yeast can produce unacceptably high amounts of hydrogen sulfide and is often a reason for somewhat limiting their growth in the must.

An interesting question one may ask is why do yeasts produce stinky hydrogen sulfide in the first place? Well, the process generally starts with the fact that yeast are busy in the fermenting must producing many of the amino acids in which they need to grow and reproduce. Two of these amino acids are the sulfur containing ones methionine and cysteine which they require for their own growth and development.

$$CH_2$$
$$|$$
$$S$$
$$|$$
$$CH_2$$
$$|$$
$$CH_2$$
$$H_2N - C - C - OH$$
$$| \quad ||$$
$$H \quad O$$

METHIONINE

$$SH$$
$$|$$
$$CH_2$$
$$H_2N - C - C - OH$$
$$| \quad ||$$
$$H \quad O$$

CYSTEINE

If the initial musts contain sufficient amounts of amino acids from the grapes themselves, ammonia nitrogen compounds, and B vitamins, then only small amounts of the sulfur containing amino acids need to be synthesized and little hydrogen sulfide is generally liberated. However, with nitrogen deficient musts, quite often the yeast will produce too much hydrogen sulfide since much of the available nitrogen is used along with sulfur to produce the amino acids methionine and cysteine. The amount of these two amino acids produced acts as a feedback mechanism in how much hydrogen sulfide is being produced. A low production of these two amino acids, due to a lack of nitrogen, causes the yeast to continually make more hydrogen sulfide since the feedback mechanism is disrupted by these low amino acid levels. This can cause the accumulation in the must of lots of hydrogen sulfide and a revolting rotten egg smell.

WHY H₂S MAY BE MADE IN EXCESS

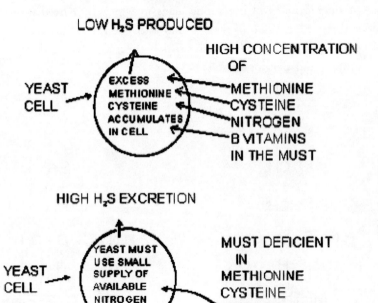

LOW H₂S PRODUCED

YEAST CELL → EXCESS METHIONINE CYSTEINE ACCUMULATES IN CELL

HIGH CONCENTRATION OF
METHIONINE
CYSTEINE
NITROGEN
B VITAMINS
IN THE MUST

HIGH H₂S EXCRETION

YEAST CELL → YEAST MUST USE SMALL SUPPLY OF AVAILABLE NITROGEN TO

MAKE METHIONINE CYSTEINE

MUST DEFICIENT IN
METHIONINE
CYSTEINE
NITROGEN
B VITAMIN

Solution

A. Although Montrachet is a very commonly used yeast, and does not always produce too much hydrogen sulfide, many new wine yeast strains are now available so why take a chance with this strain.

B. Many initial musts are low in nitrogen and even B vitamins so it is very wise to immediately add yeast nutrients.

C. Lowering the pH if it is too high lowers hydrogen sulfide production.

D. Lowering fermentation temperatures also reduces hydrogen sulfide production.

E. The first racking should occur early on (5—6 days) after the beginning of anaerobic fermentation.

F. If the must contains excessive amounts of hydrogen sulfide one can put chemistry into action to remove it by following these methods.

Solution 1—Aerate the must by splashing it vigorously 5—6 times a day which adds oxygen to the must. Then add SO_2 at the rate of ¼ teaspoon for 5 gallons. The added oxygen and SO_2 will combine chemically with the hydrogen sulfide forming elemental sulfur which will sink to the bottom and can then be removed.

The Chemical Reaction Involved

$$2H_2S + O_2 \rightarrow 2H_2O + S \text{ and } 2H_2S + SO_2 \rightarrow 2H_2O + 3S$$

Solution 2—We can add hydrated copper sulfate (available at winemaking outlets) which will also react with hydrogen sulfide.

$$CuSO_4 + H_2S \rightarrow CuS + H_2SO_4$$

The copper sulfide (CuS) produced is insoluble in water and sinks to the bottom to be racked away. The sulfuric acid (H_2SO_4) produced is no big deal since it is only made in small amounts and actually aids in lowering the pH of the must.

Amounts of Copper Sulfate to Add
4 grams to 1000 gallons of must

1 gram to 250 gallons of must

0.5 grams to 122.5 gallons of must

C.1 grams to 24.5 gallons of must

0.05 grams to 12.25 gallons of must

0.025 grams to 6.1 gallons of must

approx. 0.02 grams to 5 gallons of must

Some winemakers experienced in basic chemistry make up a 0.1 molar solution of copper sulfate and the add 150 milliliters to 1000 gallons of must or 1.3 milliliters to 5 gallons. For most home winemakers though, this chemical can also be bought at winemaking outlets with easy to follow directions.

VII. More Nasty Sulfur Smells

Some experienced home winemakers will often take certain musts and instead of periodically racking them instead leave them standing on their lees for an extended period of time. Throughout the fermentation process, millions of yeast die and sink to the bottom along with other substances such as tannin complexes. The dead yeast tend to break apart (autolyze) forming many compounds which in some cases may actually add to the complexity of some wines. However, unless truly experienced, leaving wine musts exposed to the lees often produces disagreeable odors including more with that bad sulfur smell. What essentially causes this to happen is that as the yeast break apart, they release their sulfur containing amino acids methionine and cysteine. The cysteine amino acids make chemical reactions in the must forming stinky dimethyl sulfide. Methionine has also been shown to form methyl mercaptans which are organic substances which have the O (of an OH) group replaced by S. The smell of mercaptans is easy to distinguish by most people since it is essentially the chemical in skunk spray! Furthermore, the methyl mercaptans produced can also react with oxygen forming dimethyl disulfide which at levels above 29 micrograms per liter offer an onion-like or cooked cabbage smell.

Then to complicate matters further, another closely related sulfur compound, diethyl disulfide can also be produced in the lees and it tends to have a burnt rubber or garlic smell. Of real interest though, is it can also slowly form into ethane ethiol (C_2H_5SH) which in small concentrations is onion or rubber-like but in high concentrations it gives off a revolting fecal odor. That smell is not what any home winemaker would be proud of in any of their products!

THAT REVOLTING ETHANE ETHIOL MOLECULE PATHWAY

Solution

A. Periodical racking of the lees thereby clarifying the musts is most important in limiting these sulfur conversions. This is especially true of the first racking which should occur 5—6 days after the beginning of anaerobic fermentation.

B. Only add minimal amounts of SO_2 to musts to help limit the availability of sulfur induced off-odors.

C. If the problem has already occurred, one can add activated charcoal and this porous material will absorb many of these disagreeable sulfur compounds which can then be racked away. A potential problem though with activated charcoal is that it may also remove good odors and may add a charcoal taint to the wine.

D. Add vitamin C to the must (40—60 mg/L) which will revert diethyl disulfide back to mercaptans which can then be removed with copper sulfate additions.

E. Splashing and aerating the wine will cause the addition of oxygen to the must. The oxygen will then react with mercaptans forming dimethyl disulfide which has less of an odor than most of the other sulfur compounds.

VII. Cork Taint

Approximately 17 billion corks are used annually in the bottling of wine and the wine industry estimates that 6—8% of wines bottled with corks suffer from various off-odors and tastes. These problems encountered have been associated with molecules entering the wines from chemical reactions between the cork and the wine. In fact, over 50 different chemical substances may be involved and they cause what is known as Cork Taint. The most commonly experienced odor is either musty or moldy in nature. The two major substances implicated in these smells are 2,4,6-trichlorophenol and 2,4,6-trichloroanisole. The problem itself actually begins in the processing of the cork where either calcium hypochlorite or sodium hypochlorite is used to bleach the cork. In this process, especially if high concentrations are used, reactive chlorine ions are absorbed into the cork. They then chemically react with natural cork phenols producing 2,4,6-trichlorophenol which has a distinct phenolic odor. However, this is only part of the problem since a large number of microbes, especially PENICILLIUM molds, are naturally found on unprocessed cork. Upon processing, most of the microbes are destroyed, but some mold spores may stay alive, yet dormant, in cracks in the cork. Upon corking into bottles, the spores are activated by the liquid in the wine and some molds, notably PENICILLIUM ROQUEFORT, can readily grow in wine alcohol conditions. They do not actually grow in the wine itself, but instead stay on the cork where they can use cork substances as energy sources. During their growth phases they slowly add methyl groups to 2,4,6-trichlorophenol producing 2,4,6-trichloroanisole whose moldy, musty odor can be detected as low as a few parts per trillion.

CORK TAINT CHEMISTRY

PHENOLS IN CORK → 2,4,6-TRICHLOROPHENOL → 2,4,6-TRICHLOROANISOLE HIGHLY ODIFEROUS

Solution

A. Avoid corks with lots of cracks.

B. Make sure if you sanitize bottles with chlorine that it is completely removed since 2,4,6-trichlorophenol has been observed in wines even before corking.

C. Keep dry corks in their original sanitized containers until needed.

D. Prepare corks for bottling by putting in a zip-lock plastic bag with a small amount of potassium metabisulfite and water. Allow to sit for fifteen minutes, rinse, and cork.

IX. Bottle Sickness

Well, the bottling is finally over and we are ready for a nice meal with a glass of wine. We feel pretty good about that one particular wine we have recently bottled. The color is good, it is brilliantly clear, and right before bottling it actually smelled pretty darn good! So, we bottle it and about three weeks later decide to try at least one bottle simply because we can not wait any longer for that first true sample. We uncork the bottle, and soon observe that it tastes sort of yeasty and really has a lousy smell. Don't be alarmed, it is probably suffering from temporary "Bottle Sickness". It sounds bad but what generally has happened is that with the small addition of oxygen at bottling, a bit of hydrogen sulfide has formed giving it a somewhat yeasty smell and taste, and also a small amount of ethyl alcohol has oxidized into acetaldehyde. Fortunately, this condition is quite normal and only temporary and with a longer aging period, the wine will restabilize and these nasty tastes and aromas will dissipate. Remember, as they say patience is a virtue!

The Results of Drinking My Homemade Wine Are Hard On My Body

Few have said it as well as Thomas Jefferson in regards to the love of wine. "No nation is drunken where wine is cheap; and none sober, where the dearness of wine substitutes ardent spirits as the common beverage". He certainly must have enjoyed wine since his account books reveals purchases during his eight years as President of over 20,000 bottles of wine imported from European countries. But, no matter what the alcoholic beverage, consumption in excess may lead many to lethargy and headaches. So as has been said so many times, moderation is the name of the game. Too much ethyl alcohol at one time may certainly cause some people to get headaches since it tends to lead to low blood sugar levels and overall changes in cerebral blood flow. To complicate matters, females typically only metabolize ethyl alcohol at roughly ½ the rate as males so it tends to stay in their bodies for longer periods of time. Finally, it is also possible that the small amount of methyl alcohol in many wines may also contribute slightly to wine induced headaches although this is quite argumentative.

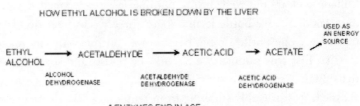

Another relatively rare wine problem may occur in certain individuals which suffer from periodical asthma attacks. On occasion they may experience a somewhat stronger attack after consuming wine. This situation may occur since some SO_2 from the wine may leave their digestive tract and travel to the lungs where it may increase bronchiole constriction. However, many in the medical field feel that this usually only occurs to the asthmatics when they are already experiencing unstable conditions such as high pollen counts in the spring or fall.

It is indeed true that in a select few individuals wine consumption may create a stuffy feeling and may even induce headaches after only moderate consumption of wine. We are very well aware that certain chemical conditions in the fermenting musts produce various amines which some are very sensitive. For example, amino acid breakdown in the fermenting musts can form certain nonvolatile histamines which can dilate cerebral blood vessels in sensitive individuals leading to headaches. Also the volatile amine, phenethylamine, can be found in wine especially if the wine has been exposed to the lees for extended periods. It has also been shown to induce headaches in sensitive individuals. Luckily for most individuals, ingested histamines are normally broken down in the small intestine by the enzyme diamine oxidase, which needs vitamin B_6 for activation. Unfortunately, this enzyme is normally inhibited to a certain extent by ethyl alcohol. To further complicate matters, a small number of individuals naturally produce less than the normal amount of diamine oxidase, and also consume inadequate amounts of vitamins. When they consume wine, their bodies then have a very hard time breaking down the histamines in the small intestines. As a result, the high level of histamines are then free to travel to the brain causing cerebral blood vessels to dilate causing headaches and also to cause stuffiness in the nasal areas. The problem is often more pronounced in women since they typically only produce about ½ of the amount of diamine oxidase as men so the problem can easily be accentuated.

Solution
A. All wines, and other alcoholic beverages should always be consumed in moderation.
B. Wine should be consumed with meals to slow down the transit of ethyl alcohol into the bloodstream.
C. White wines contain less histamines than red wines.
D. Medical evidence has shown that less histamine induced problems occur if one takes over the counter antihistamines before consuming wine.

So, from a final perspective, the enjoyment one encounters from making their own homemade wines can be truly be an exciting chemical experience and one where its slow consumption can offer many years of pleasant experiences. So enjoy the entire chemical reactions and happy experimentation to all for many years.

GLOSSARY

ACETIC ACID BACTERIA—A spoilage bacteria which can grow if oxygen is available producing high levels of acetic acid which ultimately makes the wine vinegar.

ACID. Term used to describe a tart or sour taste when the total acidity (due to hydrogen ions) is high.

ACIDITY. Term often added to wine labels which shows the total acid content of the wine and can easily be measured with a simple titration.

AMINO ACIDS. Found naturally in grapes they contain nitrogen and link together in long chains forming proteins. Yeast use them from the grapes and along with nitrogen containing nutrient additions produce their own proteins which allow them to grow and reproduce in the fermenting yeast must.

ANTHOCYANINS. A group of phenolic based pigments found in colored grape skins which are readily extracted and bind to tannins forming the colored pigments of wine.

AROMA. A general term which expresses the intensity of all of the smells particular to each grape variety.

ASTRINGENT. A description of wines that have a rough, puckery taste due to the wine being overbearing in tannins.

BALANCE. Denotes a harmonious relationship between the major elements in the wine. Acid balances the sugar content; fruitiness balances oaks and tannins; ethyl alcohol is balanced against acidity and flavor. Wine not in balance may be acidic, sugary, flat, or harsh, etc.

BENZENE. An exceedingly important hydrocarbon (C_6H_6) produced by most plants, including grapes. It is rearranged into complex phenolic substances such as flavonoids, nonflavonoids, fusel oils, and certain esters which make up many of the complex components of wines.

BOUQUET. This is a general term which is used to described the different aromas being emitted from a wine when it has been opened.

BRILLIANT. Denotes a wine that is exceedingly clear containing no visible particles in the wine. A brilliant wine can be produced through careful racking, but filtration is the best way to consistently achieve brilliant wines.

BRIX. A common measuring system that denotes the actual amounts of solids in musts or wines. Since the solids are mostly sugars, Brix is a useful way of measuring how much sugar needs to be added to ultimately obtain a certain alcohol content in the wine.

CLOUDY. Obviously the opposite of brilliant and may be due to faulty racking, excess proteins, or to the unwanted growth of spoilage microbes.

COLD STABILIZATION. An important process at the end of fermentation in cold weather wines where chilling precipitates out crystals of potassium bitartrate which will reduce the acidity of these high acid wines.

COPPER SULFATE. A common, safe to use salt in recommended doses, which will remove the smell of hydrogen sulfide and other sulfur compounds from tainted wines

CORKED. The nasty musty, moldy taste attributed to chemical reactions in the cork involving chlorine or due to the growth on the corks of molds which produce 2,4,6-trichloroanisole and various other compounds.

DRY. Typically a fermenting must will continue to ferment until all of the sugar has been consumed leaving only small amounts of non-sweet tasting sugars leftover. Many prefer a dry wine yet quite often the addition of small amounts of sugar will produce a better balanced wine.

ENOLOGIST. This term is generally reserved for professional winemakers, but when it really comes down to it, all home winemakers fall into this category.

ESTERS. These are organic compounds mostly synthesized by yeast which are well known for their fruity tastes and odors.

ETHYL ACETATE. Normally produced during fermentation in small amounts and contributes to the general fruitiness of wine. If produced in excess it adds an acetone or fingernail polish remover smell to the wine which is a good indicator of microbial spoilage.

ETHYL ALCOHOL. Usually just called alcohol, it is a waste product of yeast fermentation and is an integral part of wine due to its stabilizing properties, taste, and that it reacts with many chemicals in the wine producing many complex substances which add as a whole character to the wine.

FATTY ACIDS. Long chains of carbon based molecules which need to be synthesized by yeast during aerobic primary fermentation for the structures of their cellular membranes. Yeast also produce toxic fatty acids such as octanoic and decanoic fatty acids which can be removed from the must with the addition of yeast hulls (ghosts).

FINING. A process of adding various substances to wines to remove any of the excess proteins or tannins which may still be present after fermentation has ceased. These substances cause the proteins or tannins to precipitate where they can be removed by racking.

FLAT. A wine which has been made which is too low in acids resulting in a soda pop like taste which lacks flavors.

FLORAL. An aroma or taste resembling the complexity of flowers. Floral wines are typically made from the white grapes of Germany and few red wines contain this attribute.

FOXY—A grapey taste and smell typically found in many American grapes (VITIS LAMBRUSCA) mostly attributed to the ester methyl anthranilate. Often called the "Fox" grape its name is really not known but may relate to the fact that the leaves of American grapes resemble the paw of a fox or even that foxes are known to eat these grapes. It has also been suggested that the French in early colonial days looked down on this wild American grape and called it the "Faux" false grape.

FRUITY. Of course wines made from fruits other than grapes are quite fruity, but fruitiness is actually found in all wines including ones fermented to dryness. The fruitiness is due to the higher fusel alcohols and esters produced both during fermentation and during the aging process.

GLYCEROL. This is a small sugar substance produced naturally during fermentation and is often added to wines to smooth them out and to create a sweet taste on the tip of the tongue.

HEARTY. Often used to describe complex red wines which tend to have a higher than average alcohol content and also are likely to benefit from long term aging.

LEES. A general term which refers to the complex mass of dead yeast cells, excess tannins, and other nonsoluble chemical substances which slowly sink to the bottom of the fermentation vessels where they can be periodically racked off.

MALOLACTIC FERMENTATION. This is typically a secondary fermentation which happens when lactic acid bacteria are added to wines which contain high levels of the rather harsh tasting malic acid molecule. The bacteria can readily convert all of the malic acid to the much milder tasting lactic acid molecule thereby improving the taste of the wine.

MERCAPTANS. A group of stinky sulfur compounds generally described as skunky which are often produced if wine is left on the lees for extended times.

MONOTERPENES. A group of organic compounds commonly found in white German grapes which are noted for their highly floral and spicy characteristics.

MOUSINESS. For most home winemakers this is a nasty off-odor attributed to receiving contaminated juice from the winery. The off-odors produced are due to the spoilage yeast BRETTANOMYCES.

MUST. After grapes have been pressed into juices, and added to the initial fermentation vessels, we now call this the must. Throughout the entire fermentation process this name still applies until we have finally produced a clarified dry early wine which may be aged in vessels or bottled.

NUTTY. In small amounts a certain amount of nuttiness due to small levels of acetaldehyde may contribute to the desired complexity of wine. It becomes a problem though if oxygen is allowed to enter the wine converting ethyl alcohol into unusually high levels of acetaldehyde which gives an overly nutty, bruised apple taste to the wine.

OAKY. Either introduced into wines though barrel aging, or the addition of powdered oak, many wines benefit due to the oak adding to the wine subtle flavors such as vanilla and other nonflavonoids which impart a slight woody or smokey taste to the wine.

OXIDATION. A chemical process usually due to the addition of too much oxygen into the wine. The oxygen actually rips electrons from different chemical substances in the wine creating new substances which generally impart off-tastes and smells into the wine.

pH. This is the classic chemical scale which shows the concentrations of acids and bases in a given solution. Its main importance in wine chemistry is a direct understanding that wines should be produced which have a pH between 3.1 and 3.5. At this relatively low pH most spoilage organisms are inhibited and interesting chemical reactions occur favoring the production of sound wines.

POTASSIUM SORBATE. The salt of sorbic acid added to wine before sugar is added back to finished wines. It interferes with the budding of dormant yeast ensuring that fermentation will not start again after the reintroduction of sugar.

RACKING. The process used for thousands of years of periodically removing the sediment which has sunk to the bottom of the fermentation vessels. Racking is usually accomplished by allowing the liquid above the sediment to drain into another vessel with the use of simple rubber tubing.

RESIDUAL SUGAR. Even after being fermented to dryness, a small amount of unfermented sugar mostly in the form of arabinose, rhamnose, and xylose remains. These sugars offer no sweetness to the wine so many home winemakers add potassium sorbate and small amounts of sugar back to the wines to achieve proper balance and if desired, a certain level of sweetness.

RESVERATROL. This is a highly unusual molecule known as 3,5,4-trihydroxystilbene which is produced by a few plants such as grapes, mulberries, and peanuts to halt the growth of molds. Medical information has shown that it is a health giving phytochemical when taken into the human body.

ROTTEN EGG. The characteristic smell associated with high levels of hydrogen sulfide which certain yeast often tend to synthesize in higher than normal amounts especially if the fermenting must is low in available nitrogen substances and certain B vitamins.

SOUR. Generally a term which refers to too much acid especially in the form of the volatile acetic acid molecule which
can be produced in excess if acetic acid bacteria are allowed
to grow in the must or in improperly sealed wines.

SULFUR DIOXIDE. The major antioxidant and microbe
inhibitor usually added to wines in specific concentrations
in the form of the salt, potassium metabisulfite. In the acid
conditions of wine, the metabisulfite releases sulfur dioxide
into the wine halting the growth of bacteria and molds.

TANNIN. This is a generalized term referring to any chemical
substances which have the ability to tan leather hides. In the
world of wines, tannins consist of repeating chains (polymers) of mainly flavonoid phenolics. Many of these tannins
precipitate out of the wine and are racked away reducing the
bitterness and astringency of wines. Other flavonoid tannins
bind to anthocyanin pigments in red wines forming stable
complexes allowing the wine to retain its colors for long
periods of time.

TARTARIC ACID. The major fixed acid of grapes. It is highly
stable and is usually not broken down during the fermentation process. It is the principle acid of wine, lowering the
pH, and provides chemical stability during the entire
winemaking process.

TERROIR. A French term for all of the climatic and soil conditions particular to a specific vineyard site. It is an expression
which relates to the concept that every vineyard is unique
and that the wines which they will produce will have their
own unique tastes and smells.

VANILLAN. A specific nonflavonoid fraction produced from
oaking which may add a degree of sweetness and flavor to
red wines and also a bit of complexity.

VARIETAL. This is a most important term to the winemaker since it means that the juices used in making a specific wine must contain at least 75% of the grape variety from which the wine will be made. Varietal wines tend to be much better than the wines which have been fermented from a mixture of generic grapes.

YEASTY. Wines which have not been racked correctly or not filtered may have too many dead yeasts cells in them thereby imparting a yeasty smell and taste. Also wines consumed within one month of bottling may suffer from temporary "Bottle Sickness" due to the addition of oxygen at bottling producing detectable levels of hydrogen sulfide and acetaldehyde.

YEAST HULLS. Essentially these are the dried out shells (cellular walls) of yeast. They can be added to fermenting must where as they decompose they liberate sterols, unsaturated fatty acids, and B vitamins which are needed by new yeast growing anaerobically during the middle of fermentation. These yeast shells also absorb toxic octanoic and decanoic acids which upon racking away keeps the fermentation from becoming stuck from the accumulation of these toxic acids.

Useful Conversions For The Home Winemaker

Volume

Symbol	when you know	multiply by	to find	symbol
tsp.	teaspoons	5.0	milliliters	ml
Tbsp.	tablespoons	15.0	milliliters	ml
fl. oz.	fluid ounces	30.0	milliliters	ml
c.	cups	0.24	liters	L
pt.	pints	0.47	liters	L
qt.	quarts	0.95	liters	L
gal.	gallons	3.8	liters	L
ml	milliliters	0.03	fluid ounces	fl. oz.

L	liters	2.1	pints	pt.
L	liters	1.06	quarts	qt.
L	liters	0.26	gallons	gal.
c.	cups	48.0	teaspoons	tsp.
c.	cups	16	tablespoons	Tbsp
c.	cups	8	ounces	oz.

Mass

oz.	ounces	28.0	grams	g
g	grams	0.035	ounces	oz.

Common Measurements

3 teaspoons = 1 tablespoon
4 tablespoons = ¼ cup
8 tablespoons = ½ cup
16 tablespoons = 1 cup
2 cups = 1 pint
4 quarts = 1 gallon

Advanced Reading

Most individuals interested in a book such as Home Winemaking Chem 101 already have purchased introductory winemaking books and hopefully have found them quite useful. The following is a list of excellent reference works for the advanced winemaker who seeks detailed information regarding the entire chemistry and biochemistry of the grape to wine.

Jackson, Ron S. Wine Science Principles and Applications. Academic Press. 1994. This is an excellent reference work detailing Grape Species, Vineyard Practices, Chemical Constituents, Fermentation Processes, and even Sensory Perceptions of many types of wines.

Zoecklein, B.W. Wine Analysis & Production. Chapman & Hall. 1995. An in depth work covering all aspects on the chemistry of wines and laboratory methods utilized for analyzing one's product.

Fugelsang, Kenneth C. Wine Microbiology. Chapman & Hall. 1997. This book contains just about everything one may want to know about the yeast that ferment grapes, the Lactic Acid Bacteria, and all the nasty microbes which would just love to ruin your hard work.

Margalit, Yair. Winery Technology & Operations. San Francisco:Wine Appreciation Guild Ltd. 1990. Although mostly geared for small winery operations, this book still offers much valuable information to the advanced amateur winemaker.

Jackson, David. Danny Shuster. The Production of Grapes and Wine in Cool Climates. Wellinton, New Zealand: Butterworths. 1987. The Title says it all!

Peynaud, Emile. Knowing and Making Wine, 2nd ed. New York: John Wiley & Sons. 1984. The classic book written by the famous French enologist dealing with advanced aspects of the entire winemaking process.

Ough, C. S. Winemaking Basics. New York: Haworth Press, Inc. 1992. This is a very well written book which can easily be understood by the advanced amateur winemaker.

Windholz, Martha. Ed. The Merck Index. Latest Edition. Merck & Co., Inc. The major chemistry reference work showing the formulas and properties of just about every chemical that exists.

Sax, N.I. R.J. Lewis Sr. Hawley's Condensed Chemical Dictionary. New York: Van Nostrand Reinhold. 1987. Another excellent chemistry reference work showing the formulas and chemical properties of countless substances.